Developing Ci p

ACTIVITIES FOR PERSONAL, SOCIAL AND HEALTH EDUCATION

year

Christine Moorcroft

A & C BLACK

Contents

How do rules and laws affect me?

Respect for property

Local democracy for young citizens

In the media – what's the news?

Moving on

Published 2005 by A & C Black Publishers Limited
37 Soho Square, London W1D 3QZ
www.acblack.com

ISBN–10: 0-7136-7122-X
ISBN–13: 978-0-7136-7122-3

Editor: Jane Klima
Design: Susan McIntyre

The author and publishers would like to thank Catherine Yemm and Roy Honeybone for their assistance in producing this book.

A CIP catalogue record for this book is available from the British Library.

Printed in Great Britain by St Edmundsbury Press, Bury St Edmunds, Suffolk.

A & C Black uses paper produced with elemental chlorine-free pulp, harvested from managed sustainable forests.

Introduction

Developing Citizenship is a series of seven photocopiable activity books for Citizenship lessons (including Personal, Social and Health Education and, in the foundation stage, *Personal, social and emotional development*). Each book provides a range of activities to help teachers to prepare children to play an active role as citizens, including:

- developing confidence and responsibility, and making the most of their abilities;
- developing a healthy, safe lifestyle;
- developing good relationships and respecting differences between people;
- thinking for themselves, expressing their own opinions confidently and listening to others' points of view;
- becoming full members of the groups they belong to, knowing they have rights but also becoming increasingly aware of their responsibilities.

The activities in **Year 6** are based on the QCA Scheme of Work for Citizenship at Key Stages 1 and 2 and support children's development in the following areas:

- understanding themselves as individuals and members of their communities;
- learning basic rules and skills for keeping themselves healthy and safe, and for behaving well;
- taking responsibility for themselves and their environment;
- understanding their own and other people's feelings;
- awareness of the views, needs and rights of other people;
- social skills such as taking turns, sharing, playing, helping others, resolving simple arguments and resisting bullying;
- participating in the life of their school and neighbourhood.

The activities are linked with other areas of the curriculum where appropriate. Teachers are encouraged to use them to support the development of children's roles as members of their class, school and neighbourhood communities: for example, the children can help to organise their classroom, organise fund-raising for a local charity or find out how to influence their local council.

Each activity sheet features a **Teachers' note** at the foot of the page, which may be masked before photocopying. Expanded teaching notes are provided in the **Notes on the activities** on pages 5–12. Most of the activity sheets end with a challenge (**Now try this!**) which reinforces and extends the children's learning and provides the teacher with an opportunity for assessment. These activities might be appropriate for only a few children; it is not expected that the whole class should complete them. A separate sheet of paper will be needed for some extension activities.

Beyond the classroom

The series takes into account that unplanned experiences which the children have at school and in other places can contribute to the development of concepts and attitudes concerning citizenship. To help teachers to link children's learning through taught activities with their learning at other times, the teachers' notes make suggestions wherever possible for promoting the development of citizenship outside lesson times.

Organisation

The activities require very few resources beyond pencils, scissors, card and other general classroom items. Any other materials you will need are specified in the **Notes on the activities** (for example, computers, information books and leaflets, pictures, newspapers and fiction books).

Vocabulary

Key vocabulary to be introduced is provided in the **Notes on the activities**.

Health and safety

Developing Citizenship provides advice on how to make lessons safe and how to encourage children to take responsibility for their own safety. Specific health and safety notes are included in the **Notes on the activities** where appropriate. Advice on implementing safe policy and practice for the use of the Internet in schools can be found on the British Educational Communications and Technology Agency's website: www.becta.org.uk.

Useful websites

Citizenship education curriculum: www.dfes.gov.uk/citizenship (summarises the citizenship curriculum, offers free resources for teachers, links to the QCA schemes of work)

Institute for Citizenship: www.citizen.org.uk/education (ideas for classroom activities; links to websites offering useful information)

Citizenship Foundation: www.citizenshipfoundation.org.uk (aims to empower individuals to engage in the wider community through education about the law, democracy and society)

Association for Citizenship Teaching: www.teachingcitizenship.org.uk (a professional association for citizenship teachers)

Virtual Teacher Centre: http://curriculum.becta.org.uk/docserver.php?docid=6653 (information and resources for citizenship teachers; links include downloadable lesson plans from the Teacher Resource Exchange)

Community Service Volunteers: www.csv.org.uk (aims to reconnect people to their community through volunteering and training)

Council for Education in World Citizenship: www.cewc.org (aims to involve students, teachers and other citizens in taking responsibility for the world's future)

School Councils UK: www.schoolcouncils.org (advice on how to set up and run school councils)

Personal Finance Education Group: www.pfeg.org (aims to develop financial capability in young people)

4Learning: www.channel4.com/learning/microsites/C/citizenship (citizenship resources and TV listings)

Notes on the activities

The notes in this section expand upon those provided at the foot of each activity sheet. They give ideas for making the most of the sheet, including suggestions for a whole-class introduction, a plenary session or for follow-up work.

The notes also suggest links which can be made with other areas of the curriculum and ways of developing citizenship through everyday experiences. To help teachers to select appropriate learning experiences for their pupils, the activities are grouped into sections within each book, but the pages need not be presented in the order in which they appear unless stated otherwise. Ideas for differentiation are suggested in the extension activities and in the notes below.

Where appropriate, television programmes, stories, poems or non-fiction sources such as newspaper reports, Internet articles or advertisements are suggested for introducing the activities or rounding them off.

Taking part

These activities develop skills of communication, participation in decision-making activities and contribution to school life beyond the curriculum. They build on work from **Year 5**. The Childline website www.childline.co.uk offers useful advice on communication skills and relationships with others.

Our debate: 1 and **2** (pages 13–14) provide an opportunity for the children to plan a contribution to a debate and to take part in a debate about an educational issue. They develop listening and communication skills through writing notes about their partner's views rather than their own. If they suggest that *some*, rather than *all*, children should learn a foreign language from the age of five, ask them *which* children, and why. Challenge any views they express that do not uphold equality of opportunity. Draw out that everyone should have equal opportunities. You could introduce page 14 by visiting www.ipl.org/div/kidspace/hello, which provides audio files of how to say hello in different languages. The planning of a speech can be linked to work in literacy (speaking and listening and persuasive writing). Invite volunteers to present cases for and against the motion (introduce and explain this word). They could draw lots to decide who will do this. After they have finished speaking, encourage the others to ask questions or to comment on what has been said. At the end of the debate, the children could vote for or against the motion by a show of hands or by leaving the debating area through doors marked with the signs 'Aye' and 'No' (you could explain this traditional system). If the room has only one door, you could set up the signs on aisles between tables.

Vocabulary: *against, aye, cue card, debate, discussion, equality of opportunity, for, motion, persuade, statement.*

Evaluate it (page 15) encourages the children to reflect on their participation in a discussion. The checklist helps them to focus on discussion skills by identifying behaviour which exemplifies these skills. This page could be used again at a later date in connection with a different topic to enable the children to assess their progress in discussion skills (link this with work in literacy – speaking and listening).

Vocabulary: *criteria, discuss, discussion, evaluate, evaluation, skills.*

Winning the argument (page 16) focuses on decision-making in a school. This activity needs careful preparation, including discussion with the other teachers, headteacher and governors. The children could begin by discussing the issue in groups and considering how they would feel about taking part in interviews for new teachers. Encourage them to imagine themselves in the shoes of the headteacher or a teacher being interviewed. They could enact the dialogue in pairs and then report back to the class or record the dialogues for others to listen to. Ask them to consider each speaker's tone of voice. How would it affect the other person? Draw out what they can learn about how to present their views.

Vocabulary: *dialogue, interview.*

Choices

This section provides opportunities for the children to develop an awareness of the choices they can make, their rights and responsibilities and how to make the best decisions in different situations. The activities can be linked with work in RE on right and wrong and are appropriate for introduction through circle time.

Preferences (page 17) is about considering alternatives and explaining choices. A useful starting point is *Bill's New Frock* by Anne Fine (Mammoth). The children look for trends in the class's choices of favourite toys, leisure activities and the types of jobs they would like. Ask them if their responses suggest that there are girls' or boys' activities. If so, discuss why. What do they think affects the choices of boys and girls? Have they been influenced or do they think it is natural for boys and girls to be drawn to different activities? What happens when boys or girls prefer activities that are usually considered more suitable for the opposite gender? Point out that in the past boys and girls were separated for some sports and crafts lessons but that they now have equal opportunities. Introduce the word *stereotyping*.

Vocabulary: *choice, equality of opportunity, gender, option, preference, stereotyping.*

To buy or not to buy (page 18) is about the strategies for making informed decisions. Ask the children how they respond to advertisements. Do they want to have goods they had not thought about before? Do they become keener to have goods they would like? Nick might consider some of the following: *Do I have enough money to buy the trainers? Should I save my money for something else? Do I need the latest fashion? Are the new trainers likely to be as good as they look in the advert? Are they over-priced? Will they help me to run faster?*

Vocabulary: *advertisement, choice, decision, factor, fashion, influence, persuasion, promotion.*

The facts of the matter (page 19) helps the children to understand that texts on the same topic may contain different information or present similar information in different ways. It could be linked with work in literacy on reading and writing persuasive texts. Point out that sometimes opinions are expressed as if they were facts and ask the children if they can find any examples, such as *Foxes are not pests, The fox population has to be controlled in order to protect livestock.* Ask them to notice whether each report uses evidence to support opinions. Draw out that facts are statements of information which can be checked, and help the children to distinguish between facts and the interpretation of them.

Vocabulary: *argument, evidence, facts, information, interpretation, opinion, persuade, view.*

Animals and us

The activities in this section develop the idea of rights and responsibilities. They draw on the children's prior learning on the needs of animals and the role of charities. The activities explore animal welfare and the responsibilities of humans towards animals and could be developed through contact with local branches of animal welfare organisations. Many animal rights issues can be explored in connection with **In the media – what's the news?**, pages 57–60.

Charity choice and **Campaign** (pages 20–21) are about charitable organisations, why we need them and how they support animal welfare issues. Page 20 links the section on **Choices** with **Animals and us** and focuses on the differences which charities can make to individuals or groups of people, animals and the environment. Explain what pressure groups do (they usually focus on a particular issue, such as animal welfare or supporting refugees). Page 21 is about the ways in which animal welfare charities harness the support of as many people as possible, including the media, bringing pressure on the government to change the law and raising money to support animals which have been rescued. The World Society for the Protection of Animals (WSPA) lists news articles and press releases about animal welfare issues on its website www.wspa.org.uk, the RSPCA has information on dozens of campaigns and tips on how to run a successful campaign at www.rspca.org.uk/servlet/Satellite?pagename=RSPCA/Campaigns/CampaignsHomepage and the League Against Cruel Sports has launched the www.bloodybusiness.com website, addressing issues such as foxhunting and breeding pheasants. UK animal charities are listed on www.ukwebstart.com/listanimalcharities.html.

Vocabulary: *campaign, charity, demonstration, lobby, march, pressure group, volunteer, welfare.*

Going to the dogs (page 22) is about the responsibilities humans have towards animals. If possible, invite a responsible greyhound owner to answer questions, or the children could write letters to him or her. They could find out more about the work of racing greyhounds and their care from websites such as The British Greyhound Racing Board www.thedogs.co.uk (click on 'Ownership'). See also the websites linked to www.greyhoundrescue.co.uk (click on 'What is a greyhound?'). During the plenary session, invite feedback about the solutions to the problems faced by many greyhounds and ask the children what anyone who accepts a rescued or retired greyhound as a pet needs to be able to do. (Younger greyhounds need plenty of exercise but older ones need only two half-hour walks per day. They spot moving objects and animals up to one km away and enjoy chasing them, but tend to be obedient and easily trained.) Ask them about the regulations they have found out about racing greyhounds and whether they think these need to be changed, if there should be more of them or if they need to be more strictly enforced.

Vocabulary: *enforce, greyhound, influence, pressure, promote, regulation, rehome, rescue, retired, voluntary, welfare.*

Fishy business (page 23) encourages the children to contribute to discussions about animal welfare issues. Point out that anyone who mistreats an animal can be prosecuted in the UK, but there is no law to regulate the selling or giving away of certain animals. Responsibility for the animal is transferred to the new owner. Under the UK's proposed Animal Welfare Bill, goldfish will continue to be allowed to be given away as prizes to children if they are accompanied by someone over the age of 16. However, several local authorities have enforced local bans on the use of goldfish as prizes. The children could find out from the RSPCA and from the local police station about the enforcement of animal cruelty laws: for example, whether routine checks are carried out on pet shops or other places where animals are kept (such as zoos, circuses and fairgrounds) or whether these are carried out only if someone reports a case of neglect or cruelty. The children could find out about the conditions required by goldfish and discuss how easy or difficult it is to provide these at a fairground. Provide leaflets from pet shops or a vet's surgery, books such as the RSPCA Pet Guide *Care for your Goldfish* (HarperCollins) or print information from websites (see www.ispca.ie/petcare/pet-goldfish.html and www.puddlepetcare.co.uk/goldish.html). Before their discussion, ask the children to give priority to the needs of the goldfish and how these can be met. Is it possible to ensure this when children take away goldfish in small plastic bags? They could discuss what could be done to try to ensure that anyone who wins a goldfish knows how to look after it. During circle time you could ask the children to consider what they could do if they saw goldfish being mistreated either by people running fairground stalls or by people who won them. Emphasise that they should not put themselves at risk by challenging them. Incidents such as these could be discussed at school, checked for accuracy and reported to the RSPCA.

Vocabulary: *goldfish, needs, responsibility, welfare.*

Snakes alive (page 24) is about the responsibilities humans have towards animals and the importance of matching pets to their owners' lifestyles. It introduces another animal welfare issue with the additional consideration of the risk to humans from animals – arising from ignorance or neglect – and encourages the children to consider how the problem can be addressed. It could be linked with activities concerning the making of laws (pages 48–49) and with work in science on interdependence and adaptation – focusing on the natural habitats of animals and how the important conditions found in these can be provided when the animals are removed from them and kept in artificial habitats. Ask the children if they know what is meant by *exotic pets*. Explain that this term is usually used for less common pets or those which need special care: for example, snakes, tarantulas, terrapins and lizards. Any children who have exotic pets could bring in photographs of them and explain how they look after them or you could set up a display of leaflets and books about exotic pets several days before the lesson. Ask them if they think these pets are more difficult to keep than others, and why, or why not. After they have read the news article and discussed it, invite feedback. A volunteer could make separate lists of the risks to pets and humans which the children identify. Ask them what causes most of the problems identified in the report and draw out the need for pet owners to be well informed about the pets before they buy them. What responsibility do the sellers have and what can be done to ensure that they meet these responsibilities?

Vocabulary: *exotic, ignorance, neglect, novice, welfare.*

People who help us – the local police

These activities are about the work of the police and other local organisations. They develop the children's awareness of the role of the police in keeping the community safe, and how members of the community can play their part, especially through organisations such as Home Watch. Work on these activities can be enriched through contact with the local police's schools liaison officer. A range of material on citizenship is available from West Yorkshire Police: Community Trust, PO Box 9, Wakefield, WF1 3QP or visit www.westyorkshire.police.uk/section-item.asp?sid=4&iid=293.

Safe streets (page 25) is about the issues dealt with by the police and the level of concern in the children's local community about different crimes. The children carry out a survey to find out if particular types of crime are of greater concern to some age groups than to others. They could compare the results of their survey with those of nationwide or larger-scale local surveys on fear of crime (for example, from the Home Office – see www.crimereduction.gov.uk/toolkits/fc04.htm). The statistics from the children's own survey could be presented on a graph, from which they can identify patterns. Discuss why some people are more concerned about certain crimes than others. The children could find out from the local police what steps they are taking to eliminate the dangers (including fostering local schemes to combat crime, such as Neighbourhood Watch, involving members of the public and appointing community police officers). The children could also collect newspaper cuttings about crime: link this with geography by asking them to mark the sites of different types of crime (using a key) on a local map.

Vocabulary: *community police officer, concern, crime, Home Office, majority, Neighbourhood Watch, survey, victim.*

Crime Concern (page 26) is about the issues dealt with by local organisations. It focuses on young people's involvement with crime and on the charity Crime Concern (www.crimeconcern.org.uk). Ask the children if they think young people commit more crimes than any other group. Discuss why people are inclined to contact the police if they see groups of young people outside their homes or business premises. Draw out that the police recognise that very often the young people are reported to them when they are doing nothing wrong but that people sometimes feel intimidated by large groups of youngsters. Use examples from the news to draw out the types of crimes which young people tend to commit, especially when they congregate in large groups (a useful website is http://news.scotsman.com/topics.cfm?tid=345): anti-social behaviour, vandalism, car theft, assault, mugging, arson and shoplifting. The children could work with a partner to write a definition of anti-social behaviour, and give examples. Also draw out how crime can arise from simple boredom (point out that Crime Concern works to channel young people's energies into useful, interesting activities) and from drug, solvent or alcohol abuse. The children might be able to suggest how the solutions could be related to the causes. Information about Acceptable Behaviour Contracts (ABCs) and Anti-Social Behaviour Orders (ASBOs) can be found at: www.homeoffice.gov.uk/crime/antisocialbehaviour/orders.

Vocabulary: *ABC (Acceptable Behaviour Contract), alcohol abuse, anti-social behaviour, arson, ASBO (Anti-Social Behaviour Order), assault, crime, drug abuse, intimidation, solvent abuse, vandalism, victim, violence.*

Neighbourhood Watch (page 27) is about local schemes run by the police and other organisations: for example Neighbourhood Watch and Home Watch (see www.ukwatch.org.uk/prevent.htm). The Home Office provides advice on helping to reduce crime in its Good Neighbourhood factsheet, available through www.neighbourhoodwatch.net. This includes a feature called 'Good Neighbour Day', a day on which everyone is encouraged to do at least one good deed for a neighbour. The children could suggest ideas of their own. Ask them how they can influence others in the neighbourhood of the school and persuade them to carry out one of the actions they suggest. Warn them that they should not approach people they do not know unless this is organised by a responsible adult. This activity could be extended to the consideration of how the local council can help to reduce crime: for example, by improving lighting, putting gates across alleyways, introducing building regulations which lead to the provision of open areas between homes. Actions children should not take include: tackling burglars, intervening in cases of public disorder and going into a house which looks as if it has been burgled. Local police leaflets contain advice on what people should and should not do when they witness crimes. To find your local police force's website, visit www.police.uk and click on the 'Police Forces' tab.

Vocabulary: *burglary, crime, Home Watch, Neighbourhood Watch, theft, vandalism.*

Living in a diverse world

In these activities the children learn about identities and communities. The activities develop their understanding of basic human needs and rights and equality among people, their respect for themselves and others, membership of communities (including school and family) and about the differences and similarities between communities. They learn about the importance of respecting one another and about the nature and consequences of different forms of prejudice and aggression (including bullying). They explore the characteristics of places and communities and share their findings and ideas with others. The issue of prejudice can be explored further in circle time.

Prejudice patrol (page 28) helps with identifying examples of different types of prejudice. It provides opportunities to consider how to deal with prejudice. Draw out that prejudice is not a new problem; this could be linked with RE – remind the children of examples of prejudice in stories from the Bible: for example, the stories of Esther (Jewish and Christian Bibles) and the Good Samaritan (Christian Bible). Ask them which characters showed prejudice, and how. Point out the dates of the examples on the activity page and that the first three examples were legal at the time. During the plenary session, discuss how each example shows prejudice: the first shows racial prejudice (now illegal) against Irish and black people (in addition to discriminating against black people it uses a term which is considered offensive – *coloured*), although when property is let, the owners are entitled to refuse children or pets; the second, which would now be illegal, specifies 'a boy' (gender bias) and an age (age bias); the third displays age bias against people over the age of 50, which is now illegal; and the fourth displays religious prejudice as well as vandalism. During circle time the children could talk about other examples of prejudice, including any they have come across. Before the discussion, the children should be aware that this is not a time for naming the perpetrators but for talking about the type of behaviour which shows prejudice, what might make people behave in these ways and how the victims might feel. The Heartstone Project (including the book *The Heartstone Odyssey*) could be used for a whole term, discussing racism and xenophobia among other issues (see www.users.globalnet.co.uk/~eastwich). For the extension activity, the children could focus on prejudice connected with disability (see www.c21project.org.uk/citizenship_21/information_centre/multiple_discrimination/?FID=525162&CFTOKEN=60819723 and www.bbc.co.uk/radio1/onelife/health/disability/prejudice.shtml). Encourage them to look for examples of language which demonstrate prejudice towards people with disabilities, assumptions about what they can or cannot do, speaking to other people about them rather than to them, and so on.

Vocabulary: *age bias, ageism, disability, discrimination, gender bias, illegal, legal, prejudice, racism, religious prejudice, xenophobia.*

Action against prejudice: 1 and **2** (pages 29–30) help the children to develop strategies against prejudice by describing a modern example and showing how other children opposed it in a safe way. You could begin by reading the letter as a shared text and inviting the children to comment on it before they discuss it with partners. Discuss the example set to children by the adults concerned and how the children who wrote the article responded. After the children have discussed the report, invite feedback – what do they think children can do to influence the behaviour of adults which they think is wrong? This is an opportunity to discuss ways of resolving conflicts peacefully: for example, by using a mediator who could ask each group about their concerns – what they object to other people doing, and why; what actions by others upset or annoy them, and why. A mediator can help each side to express their worries, concerns or objections in a non-aggressive way and to present them to the people to whom they are addressed. Discuss why Protestants who live in Ardoyne Road object to Roman Catholics walking along this road. Draw out that in Northern Ireland there has been conflict between Roman Catholic and Protestant Christians for many years and that some parts of Belfast have become 'no-go areas' for one group or the other in order to avoid confrontation. Ask the children to think of ways in which ordinary people can begin to build bridges between the two communities (for example, through simple friendly actions, such as greetings and offering help when it is needed). This activity could be linked with work in geography (What's in the news?). The following websites provide background information for teachers:

http://cain.ulst.ac.uk
www.britains-smallwars.com/ni
www.bbc.co.uk/history/war/troubles/index.shtml

Children could visit: www.thegrid.org.uk/learning/citizenship/resources/conflict/index.shtml.

Vocabulary: *bigotry, Christian, community, conflict, example, mediator, no-go area, Protestant, religious hatred, religious intolerance, resolution, resolve, rights, Roman Catholic.*

No place like home (page 31) encourages the children to reflect on what they know about their identities and communities. You could set up e-mail links with a school in a different part of the country or abroad (the British Council may be able to help: www.britishcouncil.org) and ask the children to write to penfriends in the partner school. Describing features of their locality to someone who does not know it requires the children to think about features they take for granted. This helps them to recognise what is special about their locality and to develop a sense of belonging. It could be linked with work in geography (Connecting ourselves to the world), with literacy (dialects and non-standard English) and with ICT (using digital cameras to take photographs and sending them as e-mail attachments).

Vocabulary: *celebrations, dialect, distinctive, event, human features, local community, locality, physical features.*

Small world (page 32) focuses on the evidence that we live in an interdependent world. Explain that trade is one of the main ways in which people in different countries depend on one another. Introduce the words *imports* and *exports* for products and services that are bought from, or sold to, another country. Point out that importing and exporting are essential parts of interdependence. Encourage the children to consider 'invisible' imports: for example, services such as tourism, as well as 'visible' imports, such as clothes and foods. To appreciate the benefits to overseas commodity producers of trade with the United Kingdom, the children could take a virtual tour of a cocoa plantation in Ghana by following this link from Oxfam's Cool Planet website: www.oxfam.org.uk/coolplanet/ontheline/schools/chocbix/visit.htm.

Vocabulary: *buy, commodity, export, grower, import, plantation, producer, product, sell, service, tourism, trade.*

Clubbing together (page 33) encourages the children to find out about the interests and activities of different communities. You could begin with the clubs the children themselves belong to before moving on to finding out about other clubs and groups in the local community. Ask them why people form and join clubs and whether they think other local communities have similar clubs. They could find out through e-mail links with other schools. Speakers from local clubs could be invited to talk to the children about what they do: for example, a local history or archaeology group, Women's Institute, Rotary Club, Round Table or sports club. The children could prepare questions about their activities, where they meet, how often and about any special events they organise. The class could produce a handbook of local information, which could be kept in the school library and copies sent to new families coming to the school.

Vocabulary: *association, club, community, group, meeting.*

Developing our school grounds

This section involves the children in observation, discussion, problem-solving and co-operation. It develops their ability to work in a democratic way which takes into consideration the needs and wishes of the whole community. It can be linked with geography (using maps and plans) and with mathematics (costing suggested projects).

Committee (page 34) encourages the children to develop their roles as members of the school and wider community. It could be used to introduce the formation of a school grounds committee in which democratically elected children could become responsible for monitoring and reporting what goes on in the school grounds, including play and quiet areas, care for wildlife, tidiness, safety, and so on. They could also present the views of groups of children about the school grounds, including their ideas for improving them. Draw out the idea of responsibility by discussing the children's existing responsibilities at school. The children could promise to consult others, to respect other people's views, to represent their views accurately, to ensure dangers are reported immediately, to preserve wildlife, to keep the grounds clean and tidy and to persuade others to do so.

Vocabulary: *committee, democratic, elect, member, monitor, represent, responsibility, vote.*

Vote for me (page 35) develops the children's understanding about how democratically elected individuals can represent the views of many people. Draw out the purpose of a campaign poster of this kind and why it is important to show their name and photograph prominently (so that children who do not know them will recognise them and remember who they are). They could work with a partner who could help them to identify their strengths – personal qualities and skills – which would help them in the role of school grounds committee member. You could model some examples of qualities and skills to help children to work on the extension activity.

Vocabulary: *ballot, campaign, candidate, committee, democratic, elect, quality, skill, vote.*

Grounds for complaint (page 36) encourages the children to generate and explore ideas and communicate their ideas to others in the school community. They could work in pairs and then present feedback to their groups. During the plenary session each group could be invited to suggest one idea for dealing with each problem, which has not already been suggested by another group. The activity could be continued with each group focusing on one issue or it could be related to any problems of this kind faced by the school, and how they can be tackled. The children could work in groups to devise solutions and, if they are approved by the others (and by the staff and governors, where appropriate), take part in putting them into practice. Children who work on the extension activity could present their plan of action to the class.

Vocabulary: *committee, consult, consultation, discussion, plan of action, problem, solution.*

Green fingers (page 37) develops the children's appreciation of the possible costs of their plans. It could be linked with work in science on the habitats of plants and animals: for example, the children could create a butterfly garden, a sensory garden or a herb garden. There are also links with mathematics (number, money and problem-solving). It is useful to discuss with the pupils how they can ensure that the garden does not fall into disrepair after they leave the school: for example, by encouraging younger children to take care of it.

Resources: brochures from garden suppliers

Vocabulary: *budget, cost, estimate, plan, price.*

Children's rights – human rights

This section is about human rights and needs. It develops the children's understanding of fairness and justice and the meaning of prejudice. Their previous learning about the United Nations Convention on the Rights of the Child is developed as they use the charter as a checklist for children's rights in different situations. The Children's Rights Alliance for England champions the rights of the child and lobbies the government on children's issues (see www.crae.org.uk).

Doing right by children (page 38) is about human rights issues in the news and human rights issues in other places. The children might have met the United Nations Convention on the Rights of the Child in **Year 5**; if so, use this page to review their learning and to apply it to the tsunami disaster in the Indian Ocean. You could read the table as a shared text and invite volunteers to explain what each section means. The children could discuss news reports of the tsunami with a partner (key 'tsunami' and 'children' into an Internet search engine such as Google to find the most up to date stories as well as those from the immediate aftermath of the tragedy). This work could be developed to include activities in which the children organise an event to raise funds to help children whose rights are being threatened or denied.

Vocabulary: *dignity, disability, equality, fairness, friendship, human rights, needs, protection, respect, tolerance.*

Oliver's rights: 1 and **2** (pages 39–40) are about human rights abuses in the past, as presented in fiction. They could also be linked with other work in literacy on classic novels, many of which feature children whose rights are denied. You could introduce the activity by reading the passage as a shared text and inviting the children to respond. How does it make them feel? What makes us feel sorry for Oliver Twist? The children could use the list of children's rights on page 38 as a checklist against which to identify the rights denied to Oliver Twist and those which are upheld. Page 40 provides an opportunity to record these, along with evidence. The text can be found at www.online-literature.com/dickens/olivertwist ('Chapter 2').

Vocabulary: *deny, rights, uphold.*

Prisoners then and now (page 41) is about human rights issues at another time in history. Explain to the children that Elizabeth Fry was a pioneering prison reformer in the early nineteenth century. You could introduce the activity by reading the passage as a shared text and inviting the children to imagine themselves in the shoes of the prisoners. Do the children think prisoners should be given the same human rights as everyone else? They could debate this issue. Teachers could find out more from the Howard League for Penal Reform website: www.howardleague.org. See also (for injustices overseas) the Amnesty International website:

www.amnesty.org. A useful source of information for children tackling the extension activity is: www.hmprisonservice.gov.uk/adviceandsupport/prison_life/femaleprisoners.

Vocabulary: *deny, human rights, prison, uphold.*

Fighting for fairness: 1 and **2** (pages 42–43) develop the children's understanding of what is fair and what is unfair and of the nature and consequences of racism. The passage could be read as a shared text and linked with work in literacy on dialects and non-standard English (how writing in a way which communicates as far as possible the exact words of Sojourner Truth helps to evoke the feelings which were evoked at the time). The children could find out more about slavery and people who campaigned for its abolition (and how they were treated by other people who made money from slavery): for example, William Roscoe and William Rathbone. This could be developed in connection with work in history on the Victorians. The children can find out about Mohandas Gandhi and the Salt March from *Mohandas Gandhi* by Christine Moorcroft and Magnus Magnusson (Channel 4 Learning – useful for lower-attaining children), *Gandhi: The Peaceful Revolutionary* by Anna Claybourne (Hodder/Wayland) and the following websites:

www.ppu.org.uk/learn/infodocs/people/pst_gandhi.html
www.whatsonwhen.com/partners/amadeus/viewevent.asp?id=109176
www.thebiographychannel.co.uk/new_site/biography.php?id=600&showgroup=1125
www.bbc.co.uk/bbcfour/audiointerviews/profilepages/gandhim2.shtml

Vocabulary: *abolition, deny, fair, human rights, slavery, unfair, uphold, violation.*

Bully watch (page 44) develops the children's understanding of the nature and consequences of teasing and aggression and how to ask for help. Before the children begin the activity, they could explore the meaning of bullying by enacting the types of behaviour which constitute bullying (without any physical contact). Ensure that they realise that bullying is a sustained activity rather than a one-off event. Ask them to organise the role-play so that half of the group enacts the part of bullies and the other half enacts the response of those who are bullied. Invite each group to talk about their feelings. Draw out how bullies feel at the time and why they continue. What type of behaviour from their victims might stop them? How can the victims help one another? What help would they like from others? This could be used to introduce a system in which Year 6 pupils, with advice and training from experts, provide support for anyone who is bullied (and, possibly, for those who bully others). You could invite trained counsellors to speak to the children first. They could also make a map of the school, identifying areas where bullying is a problem. How can these areas be supervised?

Vocabulary: *aggression, bullying, counsel, fear, questionnaire, support, teasing.*

How do rules and laws affect me?

This section is about the making of laws. The children learn how laws are made in Parliament, and discuss rules and laws and apply what they have learned to the making of school rules. This could be connected with the school or class council.

Parliament, Party people and **Diary of an MP** (pages 45–47) are about the role of Parliament and MPs. Page 45 helps the children to distinguish between elected and hereditary roles. Draw out that the House of Commons consists of elected representatives chosen by people all over the United Kingdom. The children can find out about MPs and Parliament from www.hansardsociety.org.uk and www.explore.parliament.uk. They could also follow the links to the website of their local MP. If possible, allow time for them to watch a television broadcast from the House of Commons. Focus on the interaction between MPs, including the role of the Speaker. The children could evaluate the discussion: Did the MPs listen to one another? How well did they communicate? Did they interrupt one another or wait until the speaker had finished? The children could role-play a sitting of the House of Commons in which they raise issues which concern them. Page 46 provides a focus on the democratic process of electing representatives for the people. You could introduce this by reading *Jim Bleat for Prime Minister* by Margaret Woodhouse (Methuen) – the story of a sheep which beats the odds to defeat the goats and pigs and is elected Prime Minister, until a scandal strikes. It is available from www.politicos.co.uk/item.jsp?ID=129. Page 47 focuses on the role of an MP – how he or she spends his or her time, and where. It is useful to prepare for this well in advance, especially if the children are to meet the MP, but they can find out about MPs' work from their websites or constituency offices. Ensure that the children know the name of the MP, the political party he or she represents and the name of his or her constituency (they could look at a map showing the area covered by the constituency). These activities can be linked with work in literacy (derivations of words such as *ballot, candidate, Exchequer* and *Parliament*).

Vocabulary: *back benches, ballot, Cabinet, candidate, Chancellor of the Exchequer, constituency, democratic, election, electorate, general election, government, House of Commons, House of Lords, minister, monarch, MP, Opposition, Parliament, political party, polling station, Prime Minister, Speaker, vote.*

A law is born (page 48) is about how laws are made. You could print a list of the bills currently before Parliament from www.publications.parliament.uk/pa/pabills.htm and select one which interests the children. They could discuss it during a citizenship lesson, giving their views and listening to those of others, and this could be extended as they follow the progress of the bill over the course of the term (or longer). They can find out how a bill becomes law from www.explore.parliament.uk/cms/DocumentUploads/teacherses04.pdf (this is a leaflet which can be downloaded and printed). Details of individual bills can also be downloaded and printed.

Vocabulary: *bill, controversial, debate, issue, law, Parliament, pressure group, readings, referendum, vote.*

Make it a rule (page 49) provides an opportunity for the children to contribute ideas to a debate, based on what they have learned about the making of laws by Parliament. It could be linked to a real issue at school. Ask them to identify issues which concern them and, in their groups, to select one they think can be addressed through changing the school rules in some way or introducing a new rule. Ask them to consider how they can find out what other pupils at the school think. They could present the arguments for and against introducing the new rule and hold a referendum. You could introduce the concept of referenda through issues which have been addressed in this way: for instance, the proposal for a Northeast Assembly, which was rejected by a referendum in 2004.

Vocabulary: *debate, issue, referendum* (plural *referenda*), *rule, vote.*

Respect for property

These activities encourage the children to think about respect for property in the community, about who is responsible for it, about the types of decisions a local council takes and how individuals can play a part in caring for the local community. They discuss causes of vandalism and suggest solutions.

Not in our back yard (page 50) is about how local council resources are used and the implications of this for individuals and the community. It also emphasises the importance of consultation with different members of the community. After the group discussions, draw out the difference made by consulting the people who live in an area about any problems there and enlisting their support for any solutions, rather than imposing solutions on them. Ask them what the residents of Clean Street can do if the local council does not take effective action. How can they gain support? From whom? They can lobby local councillors, mount a campaign to gain public support (for example, through marches, petitions and meetings) and enlist the help of the press to draw attention to the problem.

Vocabulary: *consultation, local community, local council, press.*

Park plan (page 51) is about the local planning process and local council priorities. You could introduce the activity by presenting the scenario of a park which has become dilapidated. If possible, use a real example. The children could suggest solutions before reading those listed on the activity sheet. If they think of any that are not listed, make extra cards giving a brief description. During the plenary session the children could take turns to present their views about each option and, finally, vote on the most promising.

Vocabulary: *choice, communal property, democratic, local council, option, proposal, vote.*

Local democracy for young citizens

Through these activities the children learn to appreciate their local community and understand the work of the local council and how it serves the community. They find out how local democracy works and how they can contribute.

Coat of arms (page 52) uses an example to introduce the children to discussing what makes their local area special. The coat of arms of a village, town or city usually contains symbols of its landscape, industrial or cultural heritage or prominent local families who have shaped the place. Terms such as *borough, borough council, metropolitan borough* and *parish council* will need explaining. Examples of coats of arms can be gathered from www.oultwood.com, which has links to all the local authority websites.

Vocabulary: *borough, borough council, coat of arms, county council, local community, metropolitan borough, motto, parish council, portcullis, shield, stance, supporters, symbol, symbolise.*

Local election and **Campaign leaflet** (pages 53–54) are about how local council representatives are chosen and how they represent people in the community. The writing and presentation of speeches can be linked with work in literacy (speaking and listening). The children learn that local councillors are ordinary people who have a strong connection with the area (*ward*) which they represent and that they are chosen by people in the ward. Draw out that anyone who wants to be a councillor has to gain the support of local people. The following website has information about how people become local councillors: www.justdosomething.net/xsp/xsc.asp?uri=/home/find/elected/elected-as-a-local-councillor. Also ensure that the children know the difference between local and general elections and between local councillors and Members of Parliament. Draw out the different functions of the local council and Parliament.

Vocabulary: *campaign, elect, local councillor, local election, ward.*

Eyesore (page 55) provides an opportunity for the children to research and discuss a topical local issue and to learn about the importance of consultation. Each group could appoint a scribe to record the main points of the discussion; the scribe could help to keep the discussion on track by summarising verbally what has been said and asking the group if they agree. Ask them to consider how a derelict building might affect its neighbours and passers-by. They could list the things that have happened to it since it became empty (for example, broken windows, graffiti) and describe how this affects the area around it (makes it feel unsafe, encourages vandalism to other buildings). If the roof leaks this could affect adjoining buildings, if roof tiles or slates are loose they could present a danger to passers-by. This could be enacted as a role-play. They could consider how those affected might respond. What do the children think should be done?

Vocabulary: *anti-social, danger, derelict, eyesore.*

Council in action (page 56) is about what local councils do. The children can find out about the responsibilities of local councils from www.direct.gov.uk/QuickFind/GuideToGovernment/G2GMenu3/fs/en or www.youthinformation.com/infopage.asp?snID=372. Local councils are responsible for providing a police force (but not directly for enforcing law and order – that is the responsibility of the police), environmental health and refuse collection (including litter). The local council works in partnership with the police in maintaining law and order. The police patrol the area to ensure the safety of people and to maintain law and order. The council and police could work together to set up and run schemes to dissuade young people from drinking alcohol in public places and to provide them with incentives to develop other interests and skills. The children could investigate whether such schemes operate in their own area.

Vocabulary: *disorderly behaviour, local council, local councillor, police.*

In the media – what's the news?

These activities are about the role of the local and national media in communicating news. The Newspaper Society gateway site helps you to find your regional newspaper: www.newspapersoc.org.uk/default.asp?cid=251. In this section, the children develop skills of enquiry and an understanding of the responsibility involved in reporting news. All the activities can be linked with literacy work on newspaper reports. A useful website is Children's Express, a programme of learning through journalism for 8–18 year olds: www.childrens-express.org.

News sources (page 57) develops the children's understanding that different sources of news select information to suit their target audience. Do they know what is in the news headlines today? The children could visit the BBC website on the same day to see if the headlines there match those of a newspaper. Do they think the same stories will be on the front page of every paper? Discuss why, or why not. After the children have scanned the newspapers to find out what they are reporting, invite feedback and ask them to consider how newspapers select what news to include. Point out that their business is to sell newspapers but that they have a responsibility to provide the public with accurate facts. Compare the ways in which facts are selected and presented by different newspapers. The children could also look at how much prominence is given to different stories in different newspapers.

Vocabulary: *headline, issue, journalism, media, news, presentation, prominence, source.*

Breaking news (page 58) develops the children's understanding of the different ways in which news can be communicated and helps them to recognise that responsibility is required when presenting information and news. After they have made notes about the facts presented in the quotation, ask them what they think about the incident. Should their opinions be presented in the news report? Discuss how this could affect the people concerned and the attitudes of other people towards them, and whether this would be fair. They could write a news report about the incident. Invite them to compare these reports. Are the facts the same? Have any opinions been communicated and, if so, how?

Vocabulary: *fact, information, news, opinion.*

It's the way you tell it (page 59) explores how the media present information. After the children have discussed the two reports and listed the facts, invite feedback about how the same place can be made to sound so different in two reports. The reports present the same basic facts and each chooses different facts to add to this, but the main difference is in the language used. Ask the children about the opinion of each writer, and how they can tell. This can be linked with work in literacy on the connotations of words.

Vocabulary: *bias, facts, information, news, opinions, views.*

Documentary (page 60) provides an opportunity for the children to explain their views about an issue which affects themselves and society. The issue suggested is the use of cycle paths in the local area, but another topical issue could be substituted. Discuss the difference between documentaries, news, fiction and entertainment programmes. The children could conduct a survey of local cycle paths and compare them with roads where there is no provision for cyclists. They could record their observations using a digital camera and then transfer them to a computer and experiment with juxtaposing different photographs to compare the scenes and draw conclusions about safety for cyclists.

Vocabulary: *documentary, issue, topical.*

Moving on

This prepares the children for their transfer to Key Stage 3 and to a new school. It encourages them to explore their feelings about transitions in their lives and helps them to embrace this transition with positive attitudes and to deal with any worries they have by gathering information.

Turning points (page 61) draws out that transition and change are a normal part of everyone's life experience. Introduce the idea of 'turning points' in people's lives – a change of direction or the end of one stage and the beginning of another, possibly marked by memorable events such as a family gathering, a ceremony or a party. This could be linked with the children's previous learning in RE about celebrations and religion in the community. During circle time you could invite them to talk about important moments in their lives. The activity provides a format on which these can be listed and could form the basis of a more detailed timeline of each child's life.

Vocabulary: *change, timeline, transition, turning point.*

New school (page 62) encourages the children to explore their feelings about moving on to secondary school. A useful introduction to this topic would be *Going Up* by Jenny Alexander (A & C Black). The activity could be linked with a visit to, or a talk by visitors from, their next school. Through working with a partner the children have the opportunity to share their feelings in a less public arena than with the whole class or group. Encourage anyone who wants to share his or her responses with the class. The children could express their concerns in the form of letters to a problem page. Invite them to discuss the letters in pairs and to write replies.

Vocabulary: *concern, look forward, worry.*

Question time (page 63) helps the children to develop strategies for managing change. Establish that gaining information about any new situation and approaching it with others in the same position enables people to deal with it positively.

Vocabulary: *change, information, manage, strategy.*

Firm friends (page 64) encourages the children to reflect on what they have learned about change and transition and focuses on what can be retained from the previous stage and taken on to the next stage in a person's life – friendships. In addition to updating the contacts lists stored on their mobile phones, the children could update their e-mail address books and make autograph books in which to write messages when they make the transition to Key Stage 3. During circle time, they could reflect on the benefits of friendship and on how to keep old friends and make new ones.

Vocabulary: *friendship, loyalty, trust.*

Our debate: 1

- **Discuss this statement with a partner.**

All children should be taught a foreign language from the age of five.

- **After your discussion, write notes on what your partner said.**

Did you agree? Why, or why not?

My partner said	Agree/ Disagree	Because

- **Choose one of your partner's arguments for or against the statement.**
- **Write a paragraph to support or oppose it.**

Teachers' note It is useful to give the children five minutes or so to think about the statement before they begin to discuss it. Ask them to make a note of their immediate response (whether or not they agree with it) and then to consider why. They could toss a coin ('heads' asks questions and 'tails' responds). They could then swap roles. See also page 14.

Our debate: 2

Bonjour
French

مرحبا
Arabic

Hello
English

All children should be taught a foreign language from the age of five.

你好
Mandarin Chinese

Dydd da
Welsh

What is your opinion? ______________________________

- **Plan a speech to persuade others that you are right.**

Introduction

Make sure you grab their attention from the start.

____

____

Main points

1 ______________________________

2 ______________________________

3 ______________________________

Responses to those who disagree

____

____

____

Conclusion

____

- **Use your plan to help you to write your speech in full on cue cards.**

Teachers' note Encourage the children to make a list of points for and against the statement. They should develop the arguments for it and consider how to respond to the arguments against it. Also encourage them to think about ways of gaining (and keeping) the interest of their audience.

Evaluate it

- **With your group, discuss the following topic for 15 minutes.**

> Children under the age of eleven should not be allowed out of their homes after 9pm except with an adult.

- **Use the chart to evaluate the discussion.**
- **Share your evaluation with your group.**

Evaluation criteria	✔ or ✘
I was not interrupted.	
All the others looked at me when I spoke.	
I felt as if my contribution was valued.	
The others showed interest in what I said by asking questions.	
I asked anyone who had not spoken if they wanted to say anything.	
I did not make anyone feel as if he or she had to speak.	
I always waited until the speaker had finished before I spoke.	
I spoke clearly so that the others could understand.	
I kept to the point of the discussion.	
I did not make fun of anyone who spoke.	
I did not fidget while anyone was speaking.	
I did not speak for too long.	

- **Write an evaluation of your discussion.**
- **List the points you did well.**
  How can you improve?

Teachers' note This is designed to help the children to evaluate their contribution to a group discussion and the response of the group. After they have evaluated the discussion from their own point of view, encourage them to share their views with the others and to try to see the discussion from someone else's point of view.

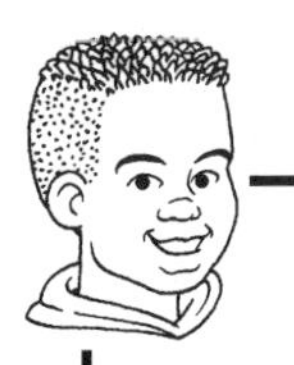

Winning the argument

The children of Beechester Primary School think they should take part in interviewing new teachers.

Their headteacher, Mrs Hunniford, disagrees.

- Make notes about why they might have these views.

Children	Mrs Hunniford

The children choose Siân as their spokesperson.

- Write a dialogue in which Siân persuades Mrs Hunniford to change her mind.

Siân ______________________________

Mrs Hunniford ______________________________

Siân ______________________________

Mrs Hunniford ______________________________

Siân ______________________________

Mrs Hunniford ______________________________

How should Siân speak and act?

- **Write some advice.**

Teachers' note The children could work in groups, first discussing the suggestion that children should be involved in interviewing new teachers and then choosing someone to take the role of Mrs Hunniford and someone else to take the role of Siân in a role-play dialogue. Encourage them to continue writing on the back of the page rather than be limited by the available space. They could record the dialogue for another group to listen to and evaluate.

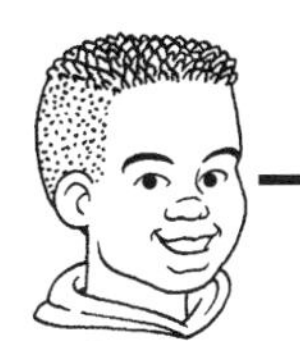

Preferences

- **Work with your group.**
- **Ask a partner these questions.**
- **Write the answers.**

Partner's name ____________

Boy or girl ________

What is your favourite toy? ____________

What is your favourite leisure activity? ____________

What job would you like to do? ____________

- **List your group's answers on the chart.**

	Boys	**Girls**
Favourite toys		
Favourite leisure activities		
Jobs they would like to do		

- **Report back to the class.**
- **Describe any trends you notice.** ____________

____

Why do you think this is? ____________

____

- **Write a report about whether or not boys and girls have different interests.**
- **Use the results of your discussion to support your argument.**

Teachers' note Ask the children if they think boys and girls enjoy the same things and want to do similar types of work or if there are differences. Tell them that this activity helps them to find out. When they report back to the class, a volunteer could collate the responses in two columns (boys and girls) on a flipchart or whiteboard. Ask the children if they see any patterns or trends and why they think this might be.

To buy or not to buy

Mmm! I'd like a pair of those.
Nick

MAX trainers – a new funky style for cool kids! Only £149
Go on – MAX it up!

What might Nick consider before he decides what to do?

- **Fill in the thought bubbles.**

- **Write Nick's decision and the reason.**

I shall ____

____

because ____

____

- **Your class has a budget of £50 to spend on activities for indoor playtimes.**
- **Discuss with a partner what you would like to buy.**
- **Look at advertisements and catalogues and check the prices.**

What factors influence your choices?

Teachers' note Ask the children to discuss the scenario with a partner and to consider any other influences they can think of which might affect Nick's decision. Which do they think are the strongest influences, and why? Will these overcome the weaker influences?

The facts of the matter

- **Work with a partner.**
- **Read the arguments of people with different views about foxhunting with hounds.**
- **Underline the facts in red and the opinions in green.**
- **Circle and join up any facts that contradict each other.**

IT WAS RIGHT TO BAN FOXHUNTING

Foxes are not pests and do not need to be destroyed. In some areas there might be a problem where the fox's natural prey (such as the rabbit) has been destroyed through the actions of humans. In these few cases, the only humane way to get rid of foxes which kill livestock is for a trained person to shoot them.

Hunting for pleasure is cruel and unnatural. No one with any morals could justify killing anything for pleasure.

Foxes suffer pain and distress throughout the hunt. Researchers have found that a hunt causes so much physical stress to a stag that the animal suffers. This is thought to apply to foxes also because they have no natural predators except humans, and so are not used to being chased.

Hounds tear foxes apart while they are alive and do not kill them quickly. The fox might finally die from a sharp bite on the neck but only after suffering agonising injuries. Many foxes have been found with their innards torn out, but no sign of a bite on the back of the neck.

IT WAS WRONG TO BAN FOXHUNTING

The fox population has to be controlled in order to protect livestock. Hunting with hounds is the most effective and the least cruel way of doing this. The alternatives are shooting, gassing, snaring or poisoning. These would inflict much more pain and suffering on the fox. Ten times as many foxes are shot each year as are hunted to death. A ban on hunting will mean that more are shot.

Foxhunting is a sport; it is enjoyed for the chase and not the kill. Foxhunters do farmers a service by getting rid of foxes which would kill lambs or chickens.

Research shows that stress and fear in animals do not necessarily mean that they suffer. The hunt itself does not cause distress to the fox because it is not expecting to be killed. The hounds chase it for an average of only 17 minutes. The kill is quick and humane. The top dog of the pack bites the back of the fox's head; a foxhound is about four or five times as heavy as a fox and has a powerful jaw, so a single bite kills it immediately.

Foxhunting protects the species. Hunting stopped in the Second World War but the fox population dropped because farmers started shooting them. A hunt kills only one fox but disperses many others.

Now try this!

- **Write a 500-word article for your local newspaper which discusses both sides of the foxhunting debate.**

Use books, newspapers and the Internet.

Teachers' note Tell the children that hunting foxes with hounds used to be legal in Britain and that there were heated debates about the government's ban on the sport. Tell them that some of the main views of the opposing sides in the debate are summarised on this page. Can they find the facts in these arguments? What do they notice?

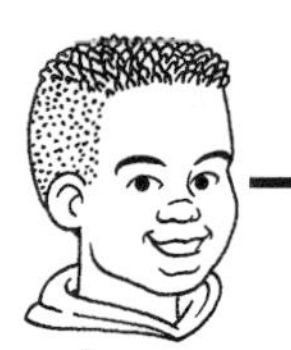

Charity choice

If your class 'adopted' an animal welfare charity, which one would you choose? ______________________

- **Write three reasons for your choice.**

1 ______________________

2 ______________________

3 ______________________

How can you persuade the class to support this charity?

- **Plan what you will say.**

Name the charity and say what it does.

______________________ is a charity which

____

It makes a difference by ______________________

____

____

____

____

Explain how it helps. Use your three reasons above.

____

____

If ____________ did not exist ______________________

____

____

Repeat the charity's name and say why we need it.

So if you care about ______________________

____

- **Write a letter to your headteacher to persuade him or her to let the school adopt this charity.**

Teachers' note The children should first have had opportunities to find out about the kinds of charities which interest them. This activity could be used in conjunction with a class or school event to support an animal charity. They could find information from their chosen charity's website or promotional leaflets.

Campaign

Some animal charities lead campaigns about animal welfare issues.

The chart headings show how they might structure a campaign.

- **Find out about one campaign.**
- **Complete the chart with details of each stage of the campaign.**

Visit
www.wspa.org.uk,
www.rspca.org.uk
or
www.bloodybusiness.com

Volunteers collect information.

____

____

The charity presents the information through leaflets, posters, press releases and the Internet.

____

____

____

The charity encourages public support through running stalls at local events and holding demonstrations and marches.

____

____

____

The charity and its supporters lobby Parliament, asking for laws to be made or changed.

____

____

- **Find out about the effects of the campaign.**

  What was the outcome?

  Did it get publicity and did this gain support from large numbers of people?

  Did it lead to a new law?

Teachers' note This chart could be used to help the children to write a report about a charity with which they have had contact (for example, through a visit to its offices or a visit from one of its workers). The headings on the chart are designed to help them to structure questions to ask during such a visit. If a visit is not possible, they could research a charity or animal welfare campaign website.

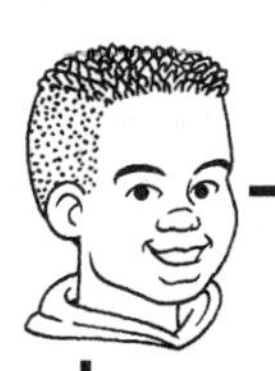

Going to the dogs

Greyhound racing is legal in the UK.

The dogs seem to enjoy the chase and they come to no harm if they are looked after properly.

Most racing greyhounds are well cared for but some are not.

- **Read the problems with a partner.**
- **Discuss what could be done.**
- **Make notes about possible solutions.**

Problem	Possible solution
Some greyhounds are raced when they are not well or fit enough.	
Some successful dogs are raced too often.	
Unsuccessful greyhounds are sometimes abandoned or killed.	
Dogs have to have their ears tattooed to identify them, but some owners cut off the dogs' ears when they abandon them so that they cannot be identified.	
When greyhounds become too old to race, some are abandoned or killed.	

- **Write a report to suggest what the government can do to protect greyhounds.**

Do some more research using greyhound welfare websites.

Teachers' note Review the children's learning about the care of pets, especially dogs. What extra kinds of care might be needed for greyhounds which are kept for racing? Ask them to read about the problems which arise when some owners are more concerned with making money than with the welfare of their dogs.

Fishy business

Rosie won a goldfish at the fairground.

- **Discuss this with your group.**
- **Afterwards, makes notes on the notepad.**

What we think about keeping live animals in fairgrounds

____

____

____

____

What we think about giving live animals as prizes

____

____

____

____

What we think should be done

____

____

____

____

- **Write a letter to your local Member of Parliament to express any concerns you have about goldfish as prizes at fairs.**

Teachers' note Ask the children if they have ever won a goldfish at a fairground. In what kind of container was it given to them? Ask them what happened afterwards. Do they think fish given as prizes are in danger of being harmed? Discuss what might happen to them and why they are more at risk than those sold in pet shops.

Snakes alive

- **Read and discuss the report with a partner.**
- **List the ways in which people and exotic animals are being put at risk.**

PET SHOPS 'NOT ADVISING CUSTOMERS ON EXOTIC ANIMALS'

A "CONSIDERABLE" number of owners of exotic pets lack the experience or knowledge to look after their animals properly, according to a report today by the RSPCA. A large part of the blame is put on poor standards of help and advice offered to novice owners by pet shops. The report also highlights a lack of vets able to provide treatment for exotic animals.

There are no official figures on the number of exotic pets in the UK but animals on sale from pet shops include birds, snakes and other reptiles, terrapins and even small alligators. The number of exotic pets collected by the RSPCA has soared by 161% since 1999, often after owners with little or no previous knowledge of keeping such animals find they cannot cope. The RSPCA, which collected more than 2,500 neglected, unwanted or abandoned exotic pets last year, says it faces an ongoing battle to house them temporarily or rehome them.

In its report, the charity says information given to prospective owners of unusual pets is often "woefully inadequate" or even wrong. In a survey of 300 pet shops in England and Wales that sold exotic animals, 81% did not ask if the caller had kept the unusual pet in question before or knew someone who had. Almost 9 out of 10 shops contacted over the telephone by researchers from the public opinion researchers MORI failed to ask questions about the person's family, such as whether they had young children.

One pet shop owner, who was contacted about buying a caiman (small alligator) and was told there would be a baby in the house, merely suggested not allowing the child into the tank with the animal. Among snakes offered for sale were boa constrictors that can grow up to 4 metres and require plenty of space and specialist care. These are not suggested for a novice keeper or someone with a young child. Yet the survey found that many pet shops suggested boa constrictors were easy to keep and none discouraged callers when told the snake would be a pet for a child.

More than 4 in 10 owners of exotic pets questioned in a survey on behalf of the RSPCA said the most common problems they experienced were due to lack of information provided by the supplier. Twenty-one per cent of the 1,124 owners reported difficulties feeding the pets and 8% said the animal was growing too fast.

A separate poll among 190 vets found that fewer than half treated exotic pets.

The RSPCA believes legislation is needed to impose a "duty of care" on pet owners. Under current law, animals have to suffer physically before any action can be taken. The charity also wants a ban on imports of animals caught in the wild. An estimated 100,000 reptiles were imported via Heathrow Airport in 2002, compared with 67,000 in 2001.

Sarah Kennell, RSPCA scientific officer, said: "If owners provide for the needs of the animal then we are not against the keeping of these pets but we are opposed to the poor treatment we are all too often seeing. Our inspectors are taking in these animals but then need to find organisations which can provide the specialist care needed."

Adapted from manchesteronline.co.uk

- **Propose a law which would protect people and exotic animals.**

Teachers' note After the children have listed the risks to people and animals, invite feedback and write up their responses. Ask them to discuss these in groups and to suggest ways of preventing them. How can people be made aware of the risks to themselves and the harm they could do to the animals through ignorance? What laws or regulations do the children think are needed? How could these be enforced?

Safe streets

- **Work in a group.**

  What safety issue is of most concern to different age groups in your local community?

- **Conduct a survey to find out.**

  Number of people we interviewed in each age group: ________

> **Never carry out a survey alone. You should always be with a responsible adult.**

Issue	Number of people who said it was their main concern				
	5–11 years	12–19 years	20–39 years	40–59 years	60+ years
mugging					
burglary					
car theft					
violence					
drunkenness					
disorderly young people					
vandalism					
litter					
drug abuse					
graffiti					

- **Enter the results of your survey on a bar chart.**
- **Show how many people said each issue was their main concern.**

- **Collect evidence about an issue which concerns the majority of your local community.**
- **Find out what action, if any, is being taken to deal with it.**
- **Write a newspaper report about the issue.**

Teachers' note This survey could be carried out in several ways: people in the local community who are known to the school could be interviewed or sent a questionnaire or an e-mail survey. Five groups of children should each survey a different age group, then show the results for that age group on a bar chart and report back to the class. Or they could use data-handling software and display the results on an electronic whiteboard during the plenary session. What trends can they find?

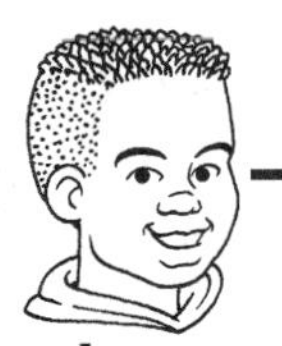

Crime Concern

Crime Concern is a charity whose mission is:

'to work with local people, community groups and crime and disorder agencies to reduce crime and create environments where everyone can lead their lives free from fear and intimidation'

One way in which it does this is to set up Junior Youth Inclusion Projects.

- **Work with a partner.**
- **Read about one of these projects.**

Eleven-year-old Nathan is a changed boy. His violent, impulsive behaviour and tendency to set fire to things were getting people down – especially his teachers at his Leeds school. But during the summer Nathan became involved in the Halton Moor Junior Youth Inclusion Project and his life has changed.

"He's a great lad," says project worker Tom Henri, "but he was very hard to control – very impulsive, you didn't know what he would do next. But now, you can calm him down and talk to him and his behaviour has improved beyond measure." Nathan agrees: "I used to be bad – getting into fights, burning things. Now I play football and go on trips. I went on a boat for the first time ever with Tom. It was great."

Local anti-social behaviour enforcement officer John Dunbar said the Halton Moor estate has a problem with youth crime: "There are a lot of drugs problems, glue-sniffing and a lot of disorder on the estate, but this summer the kids have been busy at the project. It's so good to see them enjoying themselves there and there's certainly been less youth crime. I've definitely had fewer complaints and that's refreshing."

From www.crimeconcern.org.uk

- **Discuss the article and read other news reports about youth crime.**
- **Complete the chart.**

Go to news.scotsman.com/topics.cfm?tid=345.

Reasons why young people turn to crime	
The types of crimes they commit	
What might stop them	

- **Find out what Crime Concern does in your neighbourhood, or what it could do.**
- **Describe the changes this has made or could make.**

Teachers' note After the children have completed the activity, ask them for feedback. Can they think of any other reasons than those mentioned in the report why Nathan might have behaved so badly? How do they think people responded to his bad behaviour? Would this have helped him to stop? Why, or why not? Discuss what difference the Junior Youth Inclusion Project made.

Neighbourhood Watch

When a community has a Home Watch scheme, the people agree to help one another and the police to prevent crime.

What actions can they take?

- **Discuss this with your group.**
- **Explain your answers.**

Actions	How these actions help

- **List three actions which people should not take.**
- **Explain why.**

1 ____________________

2 ____________________

3 ____________________

- **Write a leaflet to explain to younger children what they could do to help.**

Teachers' note After completing the activity sheet, the children could work in groups to devise a Neighbourhood Watch scheme for the school. What kinds of crimes are sometimes committed in schools (by pupils and people from outside)? How can they be prevented?

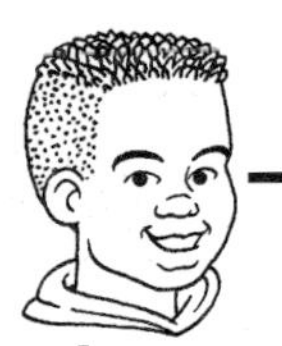

Prejudice patrol

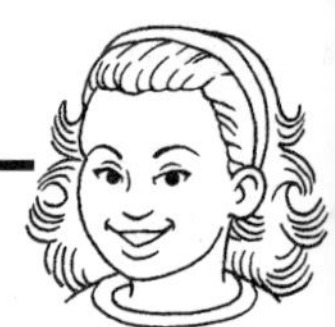

- **Explain how each example shows prejudice.**

ROOMS TO LET
No coloureds
No dogs
No Irish
No children
Tel. 70210

Newspaper cutting – Leeds, 1953

Delivery boy wanted (Age 14–16)

Sign in grocer's shop – Liverpool, 1964

Don't interview the over 50s. They'll be too slow for this work.

Phone conversation – London, 1972

Synagogue door – London, 2003

Now try this!

- **Describe another type of prejudice.**
- **Collect three examples and explain how they show prejudice.**

Teachers' note Tell the children that the examples of prejudice they are going to read about actually happened. Discuss the meaning of prejudice (making judgements about people on the basis of assumptions, usually made because of their gender, race, religion or age). Point out that these types of prejudice are illegal.

Action against prejudice: 1

- **Discuss this letter with a partner.**
- **List the facts about the events.**
- **What type of prejudice was being shown?**
- **Make notes about how the events affected the children at the school and the young reporters who wrote this.**

HOLY CROSS – ASK THE CHILDREN

October 1, 2001

To the Editor,

As young journalists we feel strongly about the dispute at the Holy Cross Girls Primary School, but until now no-one has been willing to listen to our opinion.

The notion of rights has been tossed around all over the place by just about everyone. What does 'my right' mean? The Catholic parents of the young girls say it is 'my right' to walk with their children along the Ardoyne Road. The Protestant people living there say it is 'my right' to protest against what they see as an invasion of their community.

Has anybody heard what the 'my right' is of the young girls themselves? When you are seven years old your senses are developed to perceive pleasure, pain and fear. It is unlikely any of the school children walking to Holy Cross are fully aware of the intricacies of this issue. For them it is simple – I am scared, I want this to stop, I want to go to school. That is 'my right'.

Those pupils could have been asked what they want but instead we have parents pulling children through police lines, while grown men and women line the road, spit on them, hurl abuse and bricks and, recently, blast bombs. This isn't acceptable, no matter what the circumstances.

Watching adults fumble over a community issue which could have been dealt with peaceably and responsibly reminds us that, as children, we are perceived as powerless individuals in Northern Ireland's society. BUT we shouldn't be, because we have RIGHTS according to local, national and international law!

If we had a Children's Commissioner in office, our voices and those of the Holy Cross pupils might have been heard.

We watch how our parents and our politicians act and speak. One day, when it is too late, we will wake up and probably find that we have followed and copied them. And that we have sadly made the same mistakes that they have.

If only Holy Cross parents and the loyalist protesters exercised wisdom, we could at least cling to a memory, where good sense has prevailed.

Please think before you act, because children might follow you!

Yours sincerely,

Children's Express Reporters

From *Fortnight* magazine

- **Write a reply to the letter as if you were the magazine editor.**

Teachers' note Give some background information before the children begin this activity (a brief summary of the conflict in Northern Ireland). Tell them that the newspaper report they are going to read is about a school which became the focus for bitter confrontations between Protestants living nearby and Catholics bringing their children to school.

Action against prejudice: 2

- **Work in a group.**
- **Discuss the ways in which the children of Holy Cross School could take action against prejudice.**

What could the children do to set an example to adults?

How could they persuade the people of Ardoyne Road to be friendly towards them?

What can the children do to show friendship towards those people?

Who could help them?

- **Write your ideas on the notepad.**

- **In your group, vote for the best idea.**
- **Work with a partner to describe and explain this idea.**
- **Say why you think it will work.**

- **Find out how schools in Northern Ireland are trying to overcome prejudice.**

Teachers' note The children should first have completed page 29. Ask them what the adults were arguing (and even fighting) over. Is this the type of thing that children sometimes argue over? How do adults respond to children arguing? What can children do when adults behave in this way? Discuss ways of handling conflict peacefully (see **Notes on the activities**, page 8).

No place like home

- **Plan a letter or e-mail to a penfriend in another school describing the important features of your locality and community.**

Most important physical features

What makes the place special?

____

____

____

____

Most important human features

How have people changed the place in important ways?

____

____

____

Customs and dialect

What do people do and say which is distinctive?

____

____

____

Celebrations

What events are special?

____

____

____

____

Now try this!

- **Write the introduction to your letter.**
- **Write a summary of what the place is like.**

Teachers' note The children could prepare for this as a homework activity. Point out that sometimes we stop noticing familiar things and ask them to imagine they are visiting the local area for the first time. What features and events would they see and hear? After completing their plan, the children could write the full letter on a separate sheet of paper or as an e-mail attachment.

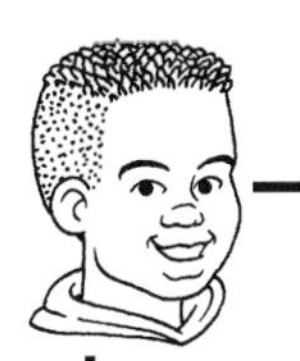

Small world

- **Work with a group.**
- **Write the names of countries on the flags.**
- **Along each arrow, write some things the United Kingdom buys from each country.**

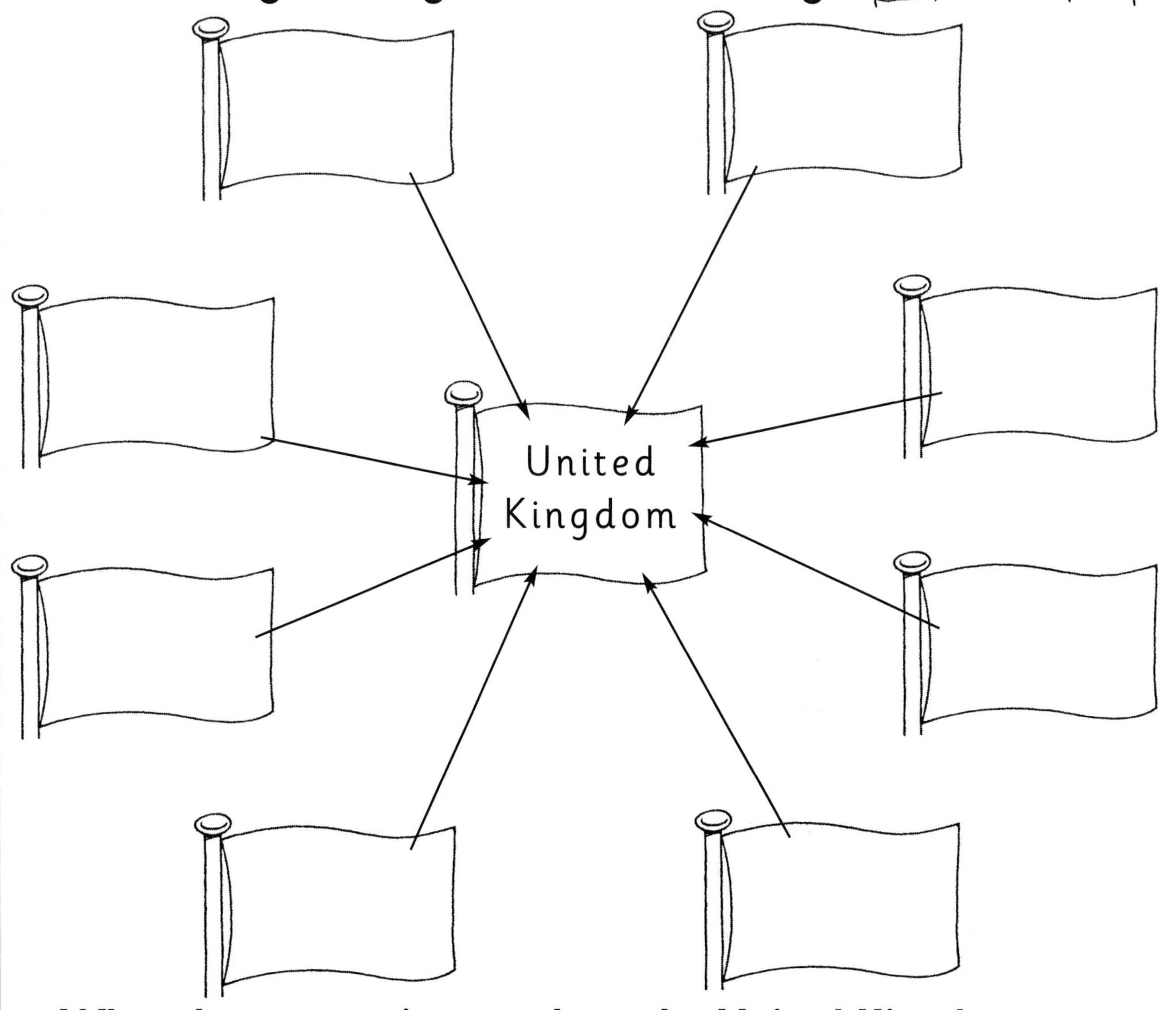

What does exporting goods to the United Kingdom mean to workers abroad? ______________________

____

- **Find out more about one of the countries.**
- **Write an article about its trade with another country.**

Teachers' note Ask the children to prepare for this as a homework activity over about a week by reading labels on goods, clothes and food at home and noticing which countries they come from and any trends (for example, cocoa from Ghana, audio equipment from Japan, fruit from Israel, vegetables from Spain, clothes from Taiwan).

Clubbing together

Why do people form clubs?

- **Find out about the clubs that meet in your local community.**

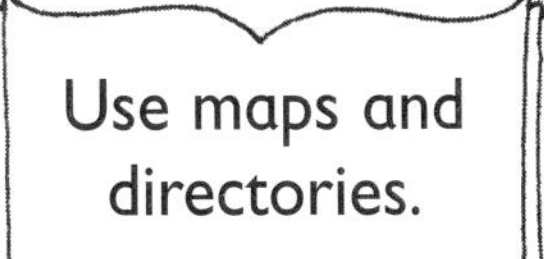

Ask people you know.

Club	Where it meets	How often it meets	Age group of members	What they do

What new club would you like at school?

- **Write your ideas about the club and what the members would do.**

Teachers' note The children could find out about the clubs and associations in the local area from directories, local newspapers, radio and television news or feature programmes and from people they know. When they have completed the activity, ask them what they notice about why people have formed these clubs: for example, to play sports and games, to share information about a hobby or interest, to help charities, to support a political party.

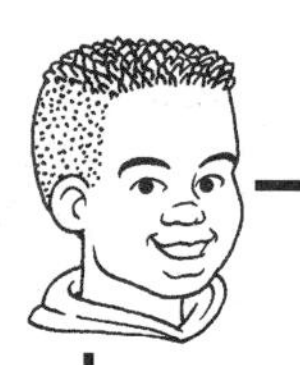

Committee

- **Work in a group.**
- **Discuss what a pupils' school grounds committee should aim to do.**
- **List the committee's main aims and responsibilities.**

Aims	Responsibilities

What could the committee do to achieve these aims and fulfil these responsibilities?

What should the committee members promise to do?

- **Write a committee promise.**

As a member of the school grounds committee, I promise

- **Design an advertisement to encourage children to join the school grounds committee.**

Teachers' note Ask the children who decides what happens to the school grounds: for example, the siting of litter bins, seats and play equipment, checking for wear and tear and safety and finding out if any changes are needed. Point out that the children can help by observing how the grounds are used, whether any areas are over- or under-used and finding out why.

Vote for me

- **Describe yourself as a candidate for election to the school grounds committee.**

Candidate for the School Grounds Committee	
Name	Age Class
Why I want to be a committee member	A photograph of me
My personal qualities and skills which would help me	Other information

- **Write some examples to show your personal qualities and skills.**

Teachers' note Discuss what the children know about choosing others to act on their behalf. Explain that anyone could be a committee member – everyone has something to contribute. Talk about what a school grounds committee member would need to do. What personal qualities and skills would be useful? Point out that few people have all the qualities and skills needed, but everyone has some of them.

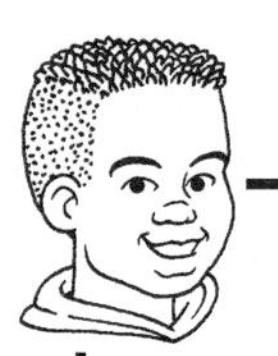

Grounds for complaint

These children's school grounds were being damaged.

(a) We couldn't go on the field because cows had got into it.

(b) Someone has broken the fence.

(c) People throw litter over our playground wall.

(d) People walk dogs here. The dogs foul the field and garden.

(e) Someone stole the best bench.

(f) There are deep potholes in the playground. They fill with water when it rains.

What could the school grounds committee do?

- **Discuss this with a partner.**

Problem	Possible solution
a	
b	
c	
d	
e	
f	

- **Write a plan of action to tackle one of the problems.**

Teachers' note It is useful to acknowledge that, although these are all real examples of damage to a school environment, few schools would suffer from all of them. Ask the children which result from intentional vandalism and which are the result of thoughtlessness or people being unaware of the damage they were doing. Discuss how this could affect the solutions to the problems.

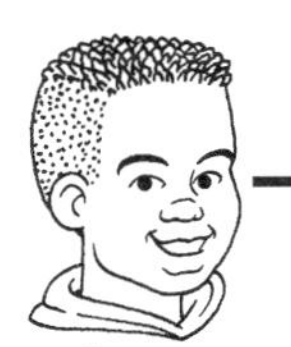

Green fingers

- **Work with a group.**
- **Use this page to plan a small garden.**
- **Write your budget here.** ______
- **Draw a plan of the garden.**

You need

garden supplies catalogues and price lists

a calculator

Try out your ideas on scrap paper first.

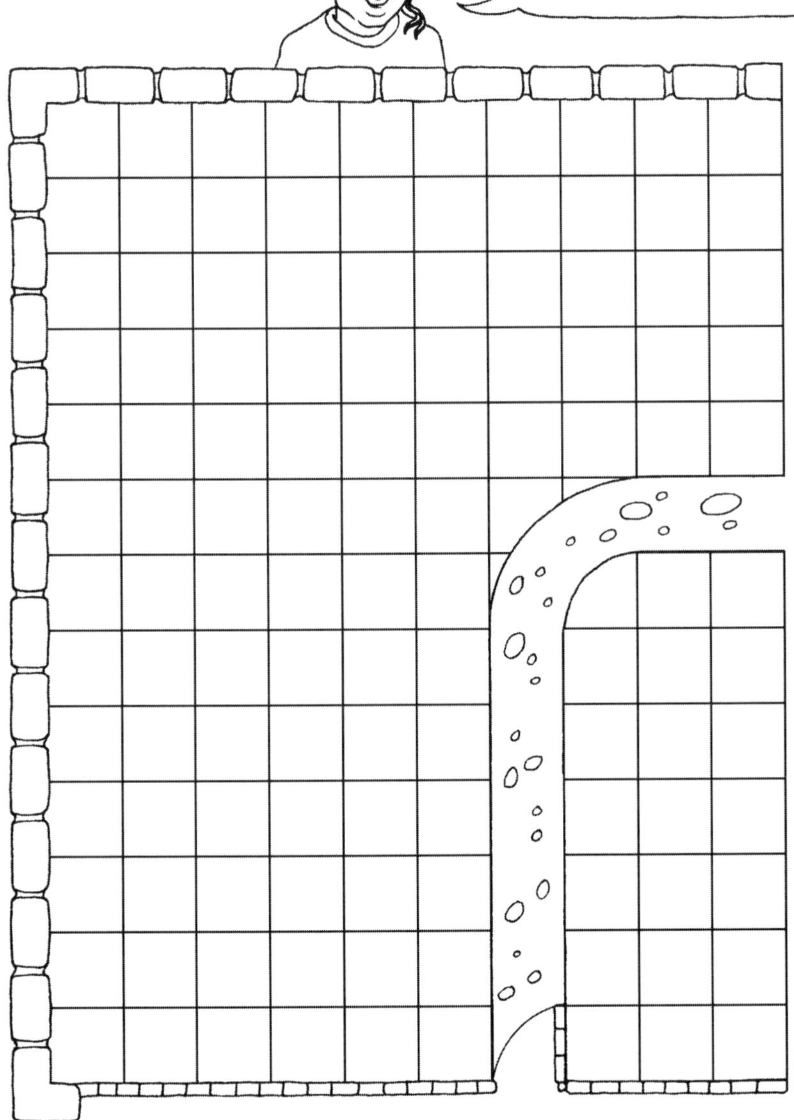

Scale 1:100

- **List what you need to buy.**

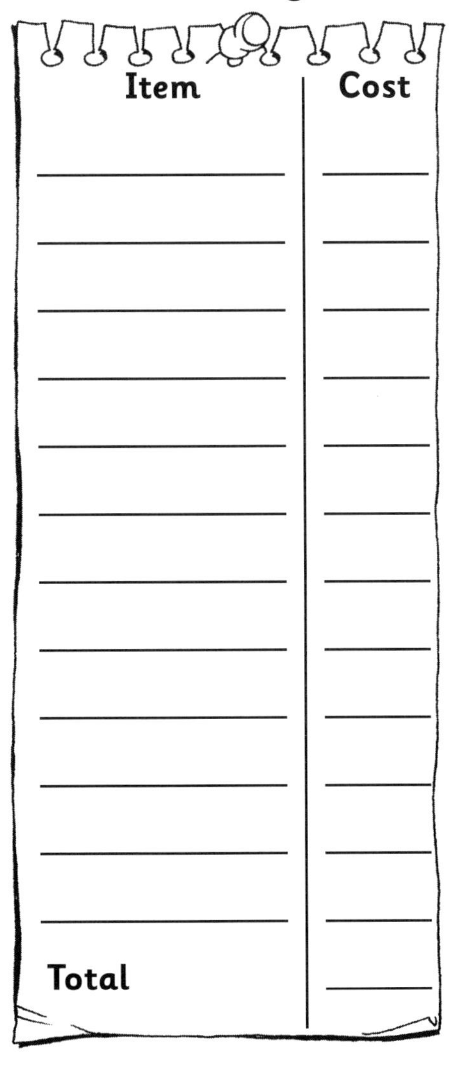

Item	Cost
Total	

- **Find ways of reducing the cost by 25 per cent.**

Teachers' note This could be used in conjunction with the planning of a small garden at school (it could be as small as two or three square metres). Ask the children to consider the site and its surroundings and how the garden would fit in with them. They should also consider the purpose of the garden: for example, decorative, commemorative or functional (for herbs or vegetables, attracting wildlife, and so on) and the effect they want to create: calm, lively, perfumed.

Doing right by children

- **Work with a partner.**
- **Find out about the Indian Ocean tsunami in 2004.**
- **Cut out the news quotations and glue them onto card.**
- **Cut out the Rights of the Child and glue them onto different coloured card.**
- **Match each news quotation to a Right of the Child.**

Quotations from news reports	The Rights of the Child
One in eight children is not getting enough to eat.	All children should be treated equally and have their race and religion respected.
Of all the problems in the tsunami zone, the most urgent is the plight of the orphans.	All children should have good health and be free to develop normally.
In the relief camps, aid organisations are setting up classes and games – anything that lets children be children at least for a few hours a day.	All children should have a name and nationality.
Police arrested a man in Sri Lanka who tried to sell two girls to foreigners after their mother was killed and their home destroyed.	All children should have clean water, good food, housing and medical care.
"We need to have respect for these children and for their local culture," an aid worker said.	Disabled children should receive special care.
Children are at the highest risk from the diseases that follow in the wake of a natural disaster.	All children should have love and understanding, preferably from their own family.
"Out in the schoolyard, the kids were happy to introduce themselves. They invited me to join their game. And for a moment, at least, we all had something to smile about," a volunteer said.	All children should have free education and a chance to play and develop.
Aid workers are working flat out to try to identify and register the 'lost children' of the tsunami.	Children should always be the first to be given help.
Workers are urgently building a special shelter for disabled children after the tidal waves swept away their care home.	Children should be protected against cruelty and exploitation.
Three weeks after the tsunami hit, children and parents are still struggling to find each other.	Children should be shown and taught peace and tolerance and friendship.

- **List three of the tsunami orphans' rights that might be threatened by foreign adoption, and give reasons.**

Teachers' note The children should discuss each Rights of the Child card in pairs before deciding with which news report to match it. They could also apply the list of children's rights to the story in **Action against prejudice: 1**, page 29, and explain which rights were denied to the children of Holy Cross School during the confrontations.

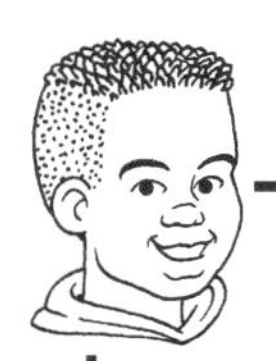

Oliver's rights: 1

Oliver Twist by Charles Dickens

Oliver Twist's mother was a poor woman who came to a workhouse to give birth to a baby. She died without saying who she was or giving a name to the baby. The parish beadle, Mr Bumble, made up a name for the baby boy – Oliver Twist – and he was brought up in an orphanage, where the children were always hungry and were often beaten. At the age of nine Oliver was taken to the workhouse.

Mr. Bumble gave him a tap on the head, with his cane, to wake him up: and another on the back to make him lively: and bidding him follow, conducted him into a large whitewashed room, where eight or ten fat gentlemen were sitting round a table. At the top of the table, seated in an armchair rather higher than the rest, was a particularly fat gentleman with a very round, red face.

'Bow to the board,' said Bumble. Oliver brushed away two or three tears that were lingering in his eyes; and seeing no board but the table, fortunately bowed to that.

'What's your name, boy?' said the gentleman in the high chair.

Oliver was frightened at the sight of so many gentlemen, which made him tremble: and the beadle gave him another tap behind, which made him cry. These two causes made him answer in a very low and hesitating voice; whereupon a gentleman in a white waistcoat said he was a fool.

'Boy,' said the gentleman in the high chair, 'listen to me. You know you're an orphan, I suppose?'

'What's that, sir?' inquired poor Oliver.

'The boy is a fool – I thought he was,' said the gentleman in the white waistcoat.

'Hush!' said the gentleman who had spoken first. 'You know you've got no father or mother, and that you were brought up by the parish, don't you?'

'Yes, sir,' replied Oliver, weeping bitterly.

'What are you crying for?' inquired the gentleman in the white waistcoat. And to be sure it was very extraordinary. What could the boy be crying for?

'Well! You have come here to be educated, and taught a useful trade,' said the red-faced gentleman in the high chair.

'So you'll begin to pick oakum to-morrow morning at six o'clock,' added the surly one in the white waistcoat.

Teachers' note The children need the list of children's rights on page 38 for reference. They could enact this passage from *Oliver Twist* in their groups before discussing how Oliver must have felt and the responses of the adults to this. What were their main concerns? How did these affect Oliver's human rights? (Explain that 'picking oakum' meant unpicking strands of old rope so that they could be re-used.)

Oliver's rights: 2

Which of Oliver's rights were being upheld, and how?

Which of his rights were being denied, and how?

- **Discuss these questions with a partner.**
- **Write your answers on the placards.**

Rights upheld	Evidence

Rights denied	Evidence

Which of Oliver's rights do we not know about from this passage?

- **Find out more from Chapter 2 of the book.**

Teachers' note The children need copies of pages 38 and 39 and a copy of *Oliver Twist* (printed or online – see **Notes on the activities**, page 9). They should use the list of children's rights on page 38 as a checklist and look for evidence in the passage on page 39 for human rights being upheld or denied.

Prisoners then and now

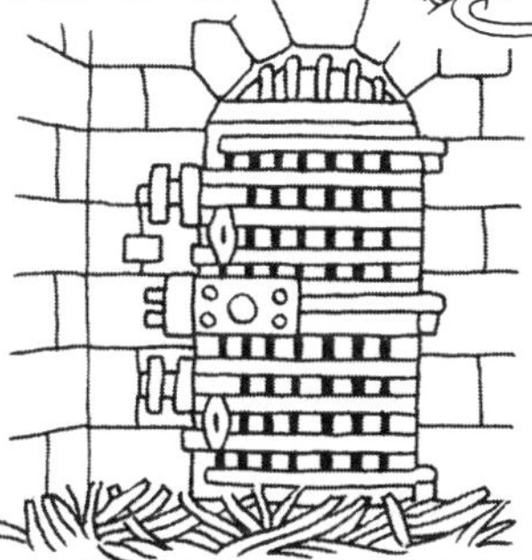

- **Work in a group.**
- **Discuss the ways in which Newgate Prison would need to change to uphold the human rights of all the prisoners.**

ELIZABETH FRY'S VISIT TO NEWGATE PRISON IN 1813

She saw about 400 women, with their children, crammed into four unheated, unlit, windowless rooms. They were dressed in rags, covered with lice and surrounded by dirt. A woman was stripping the clothes off a dead baby to give them to another child.

They had no bedding, no toilets and no facilities for washing. The daily food ration was one small loaf of bread per person – unless people brought in food for them. Fights over food were common. Sick women were dumped on dirty straw and many died from typhus. There were no medicines, doctor or nurse.

The turnkeys sold cheap gin to the women, many of whom were drunk. Some were so mentally disturbed that they would hurt one another and themselves. There were fights every day, no discipline and bullies took charge.

Women were brought to Newgate from county prisons to await transportation and kept there for weeks or months until there was a place on a ship. Many of them were restrained by leg irons if they could not afford to pay the prison keeper for 'easement'.

On her first visit Elizabeth Fry gave out clothes for the babies and comforted the ill prisoners. The next day she brought more clothing and clean straw for the sick to lie on.

In 1817, Elizabeth formed a committee of women named the *Association for the Improvement of the Female Prisoners in Newgate*. They organised classes in knitting and sewing for the women and a school for their children, and provided materials so that the prisoners could sew, knit and make goods for sale. Soon the prisoners began to earn money to pay for everyday needs such as soap and food.

- **Summarise the main points of your discussion on a table like this:**

Human right	Change needed

- **Find out about conditions in a modern women's prison.**
- **Write a comparison between the modern prison and Newgate in 1813.**

Teachers' note Review the children's previous learning about human rights. They could list everything to which they think all human beings have a right, including basic needs, and write a checklist. Which human rights were being upheld for the prisoners at Newgate? Ask them to look for evidence. Which human rights were being denied to them? What evidence is there of human rights abuse? The children could make a larger copy of the table or you could enlarge the page to A3.

Fighting for fairness: 1

- **List the examples of unfairness in the passage.**
- **Classify them as racism, gender-bias or withholding of human rights.**
- **Explain what was unfair.**

Sojourner Truth was a freed black slave, born in New York in about 1797. She began to speak in public against slavery, moving her audiences with accounts of the treatment and crowded living conditions of slaves. She spoke of the degrading auctions at which they were forced to strip for inspection so that buyers could look for the marks of the whip or of wrist or leg irons, to see if the slave had been punished and therefore was disobedient.

A heckler once called out that her anti-slavery talk did not bother him any more than the bite of a flea, and she replied, 'Perhaps not but, Lord willing, I'll keep you scratching.'

This is a passage from a famous speech which she made:

'Dat man ober dar say dat womin needs to be helped into carriages, and lifted ober ditches, and to hab de best place everywhar. Nobody eber helps me into carriages, or ober mud-puddles, or gibs me any best place! And ain't I a woman? Look at me! Look at my arm! I have ploughed, and planted and gathered into barns, and no man could head me! And ain't I a woman? I could work as much and eat as much as a man – when I could get it – and bear de lash as well! And ain't I a woman? I have borne thirteen chilern, and seen 'em mos' all sold off to slavery, and when I cried out with my mother's grief, none but Jesus heard me! And ain't I a woman?'

Example of unfairness	Type of unfairness	What made it unfair

- **Make notes about a modern-day example of racism, gender-bias or human rights violations.**
- **Write a report about it for your class to read.**

Teachers' note Read the passage with the children. How do they feel when they read Sojourner Truth's speech? How might audiences at the time have felt? Point out that some of the people who heard her would have supported slavery and might have had slaves themselves. Others might have been slaves (or former slaves).

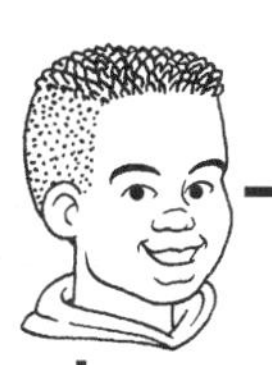

Fighting for fairness: 2

- **Find out how Mohandas Gandhi took action to help people who were treated unfairly.**

You could read about the Salt March.

Gandhi's dates

People being treated unfairly

Place

What was unfair

What made Gandhi decide to help?

What Gandhi did

The difference it made

- **Write part of a biography about Gandhi which shows how he encouraged other people to support his cause.**

Teachers' note This page could be used in conjunction with work in history or RE. See **Notes on the activities**, page 10, for sources of information.

Bully watch

- **Complete the questionnaire.**
- **Tick the box if the answer is yes.**

You need not give your name.

Have you been bullied at school?	
Was it done by children of your own age?	
Was the bullying in the form of words (insults or name-calling)?	
Was it sent as a text message?	
Was it physical (for example, hair-pulling, hitting, kicking, pinching, punching or pushing)?	
Were there threats to harm you?	
Was it racist (because of your colour, race or religion)?	
Did the bullying keep you from friendships?	
Did you tell a teacher or other adult at school?	
Did you tell your parents or carers?	
Did you tell a friend, playground buddy or school council member?	
Did you fight back (by hitting or with words)?	
Did you stay off school?	

- **Put your questionnaire into a pile to be shuffled and discussed by the class.**
- **Present the results in a graph.**
- **Ask questions about the results, such as:**

You could use data handling software.

How many children in this class have been bullied? ______

What is the most common form of bullying? ________________

Do most children report bullying? ________

- **Write your ideas for tackling bullying in your school.**
- **Use the results of the questionnaire to support your suggestions.**

Teachers' note The children should complete the questionnaire individually and anonymously and the completed sheets could be passed around the class for the results to be compiled. Ask them whose responsibility it is to prevent bullying at school. How can the children help? Draw out that everyone can contribute and that the children themselves are more likely to know if bullying is going on, and what forms it takes, than are the adults.

Parliament

The United Kingdom Parliament consists of the monarch, the House of Lords and the House of Commons.

- **Fill in the information about Parliament.**

The monarch

Glue the monarch's photo here	Name ______________________________ How a person becomes the monarch ______________________________ ______________________________

	House of Lords	House of Commons
Number of members		
How they become members of Parliament		
How long they can serve as members of Parliament		
The role of the House		

- **Compare the roles of the monarch and the Prime Minister.**

  What differences and similarities can you find?

Teachers' note Ask the children if they know what *monarch* means. They could look it up. Who is the present monarch of the United Kingdom? Discuss how she became the monarch and how this is different from the way in which someone becomes Prime Minister. The children can find out more about the monarchy, Prime Minister and Parliament from the Internet (see **Notes on the activities**, page 10).

Party people

How do people become Members of Parliament in the House of Commons?

- **Fill in the chart by answering the questions in the speech bubbles.**

Who can vote?

How many candidates can they vote for?

Voters	Candidates

Who can be a candidate?

What have they to do with political parties?

General Election

Are MPs paid?

Do they have to go to the House of Commons every day?

The House of Commons

How many candidates become MPs?

What makes one political party 'the winner' of the election?

How is the Prime Minister chosen?

What is the Cabinet?

- **List the titles of three Cabinet members and describe what they do.**

Teachers' note Review the children's understanding of the terms *Parliament, House of Commons, Prime Minister, political party, election* and *candidate*. They can find the information they need for this page from the Parliament website www.explore.parliament.uk. To save time on the Internet, different children could locate and print different information and share it with the others.

Diary of an MP

- **Find out about the work of your local MP.**
- **Fill in the diary to show what the MP did (and where) during any week.**

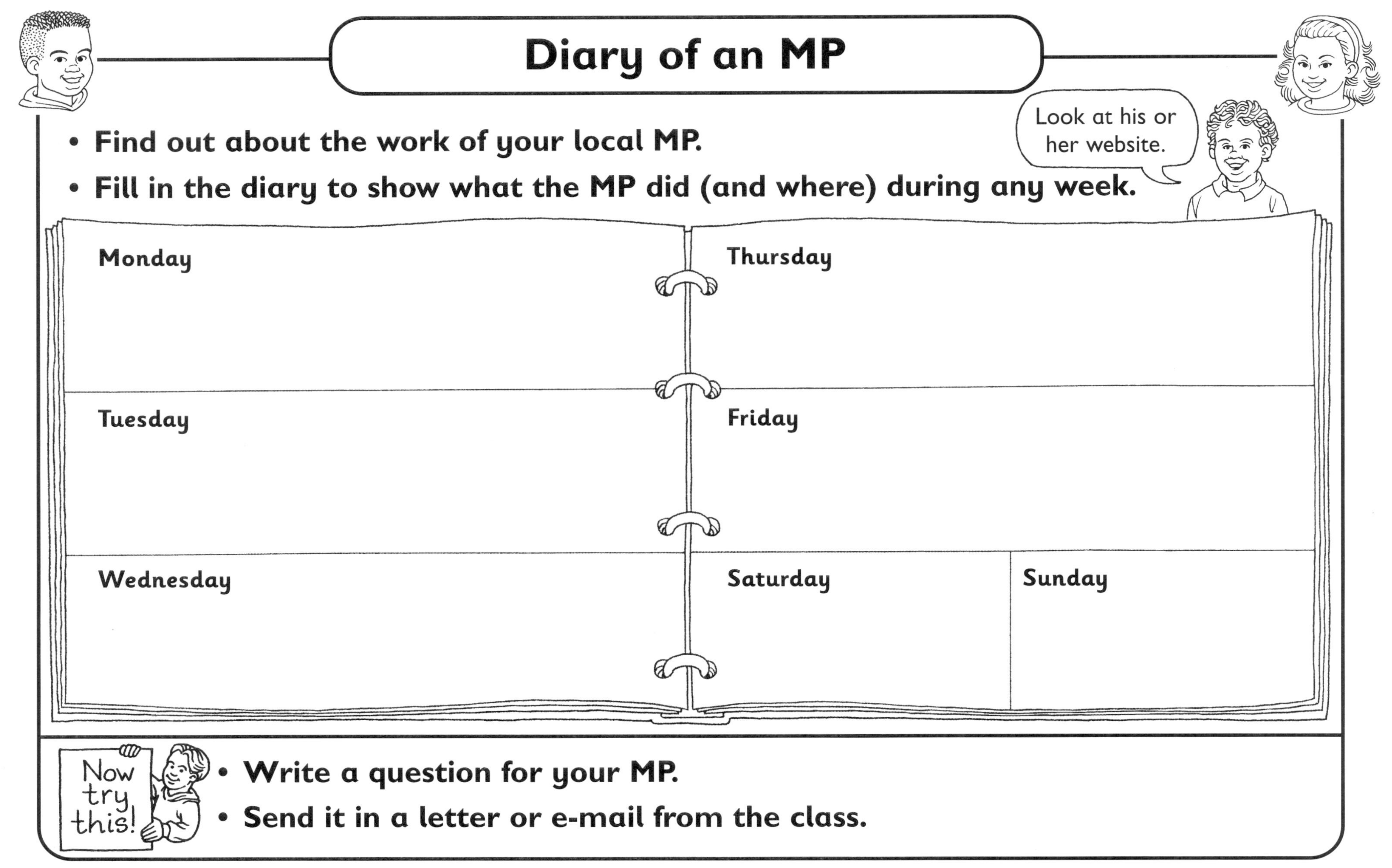

- **Write a question for your MP.**
- **Send it in a letter or e-mail from the class.**

Teachers' note The children can find out about the local MP for the constituency in which the school is situated from his or her website, using links from www.locata.co.uk/commons.

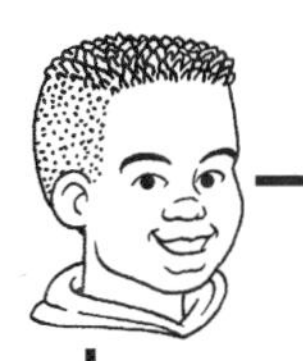

A law is born

A bill is a proposal for a new law. It goes through several stages before it becomes law.

- **Work in a group.**
- **Discuss which bill you want to follow through Parliament.**
- **Write about each stage on the flow chart.**

Certain types of law can also be made by the Northern Ireland Assembly, Scottish Parliament or Welsh Assembly.

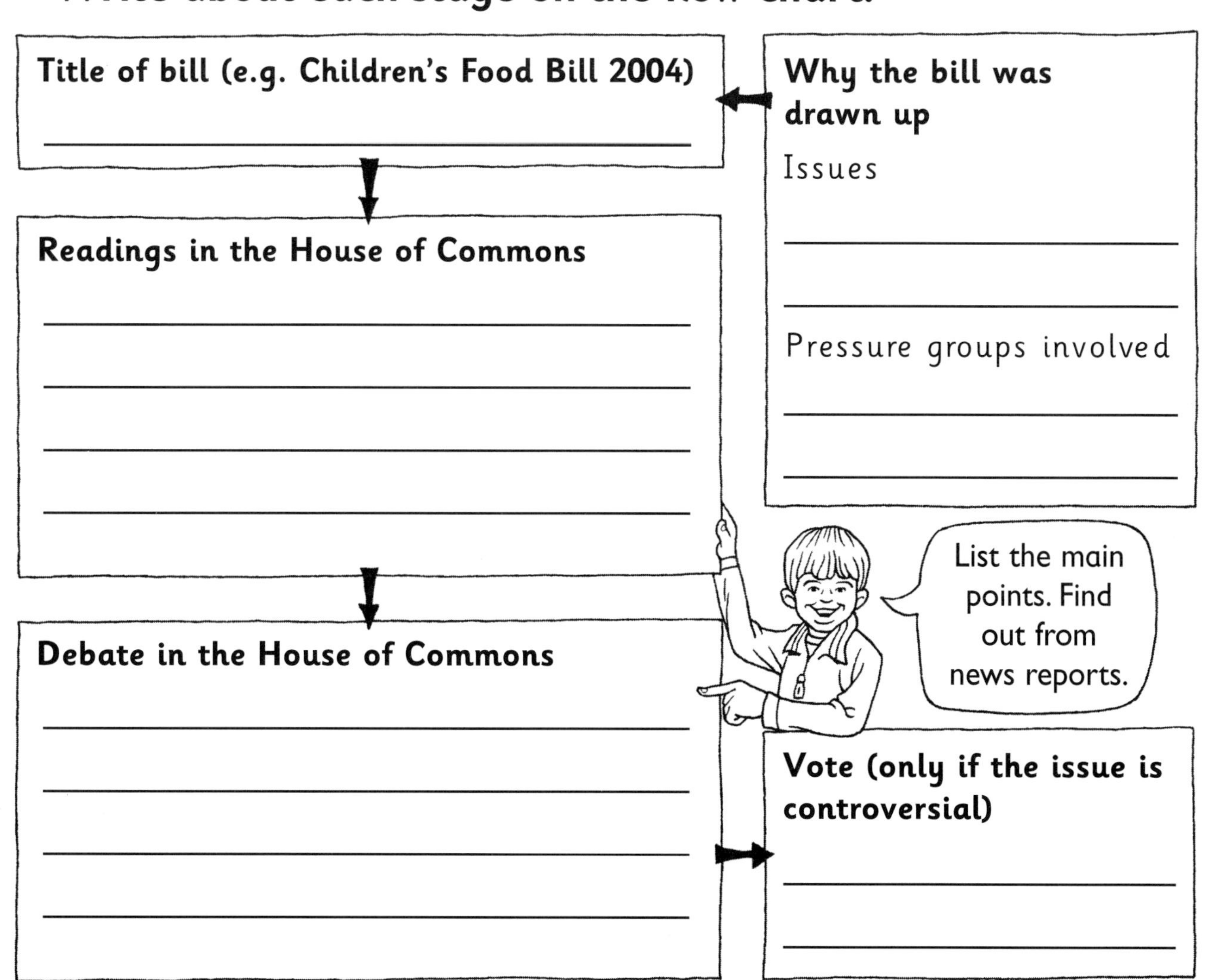

Title of bill (e.g. Children's Food Bill 2004)
Why the bill was drawn up
Issues
Pressure groups involved
Readings in the House of Commons
List the main points. Find out from news reports.
Debate in the House of Commons
Vote (only if the issue is controversial)

- **Find out what happens after the House of Commons debate (and vote, if there is one).**
- **Copy the flow chart and continue it to show how a bill becomes an Act of Parliament (law).**

Teachers' note You could prepare for this by watching television broadcasts of the House of Commons in action. Discuss what is going on and draw out what Parliament is for. Allow five minutes for the children to read the page and ascertain what the task requires them to do and to check that they understand the vocabulary used. A list of all the current bills before Parliament can be found on www.explore.parliament.uk/parliament.aspx?id=4.

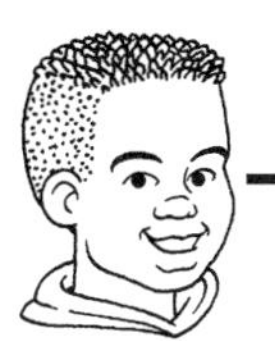

Make it a rule

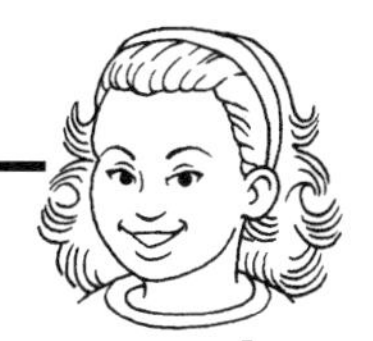

What change in the rules would improve your school?

- **Discuss this with your group.**
- **Write notes about your discussion.**

Examples:
rules about
lateness, uniforms,
packed lunch,
mobile phones,
using toilets.

The change we want

____

____

Why we want it

____

____

- **Write a bill to read to the class.**

____

____

____

____

____

____

____

____

- **Debate the bill.**
- **Take a vote.**

Now
try this!

- **Write a letter asking your headteacher to consider the bill.**

Teachers' note Remind the children of what they learned about how laws are made in Parliament (page 48) and ask them to use a similar process in their group and then, as a class, to propose a change to the school rules. Point out that in order to do this they will need to collect evidence that the change is needed and to persuade other people of its usefulness.

Not in our back yard

- **Discuss the problems faced by the residents of Clean Street.**

The council charges £5 to collect large items of rubbish.

We are allowed one bin per household. It is emptied once a fortnight.

We have to take the bin out on to the pavement. If we are out all day, it is there all day.

The refuse collectors leave behind anything which is not in the bin.

The place is such a mess that there is no point in trying to keep it tidy.

What has made the area so messy?

____

____

____

____

____

What could be done about it?

Involve the people who live there.

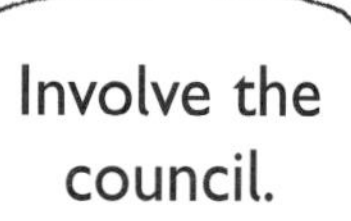

Involve the council.

____

____

____

____

____

____

- **Write a questionnaire to send to people who live in Clean Street.**

Teachers' note Ask volunteers to read aloud the quotations. Ask them how the people feel about their neighbourhood. Do the quotations sound realistic? The children could relate them to their own experiences. What could be done to improve matters? Draw out that people can take action to improve their neighbourhood. What difference could they make? How would this affect their feelings about the place where they live?

Park plan

The park is an eyesore.

- Work with a group.
- Cut out the proposals under consideration by the council.
- Sort the cards according to whether the ideas:
  – cost money, save money or earn money
  – are good for local people or bad for local people.
- Discuss the ideas with your group.
- Make notes about how each would affect the area and the people.

Do nothing.	Clear the rubbish and leave it to develop as a wildlife area.	Build council homes on the land and then rent them out.
Sell the land to a property developer for a superstore.	Build an indoor leisure centre on the land.	Turn it into a public outdoor sports ground with changing rooms, tennis courts, tracks and pitches.
Sell it to a property developer for a private leisure club.	Clear up and refurbish the park.	Make it into a car park to meet the shortage of parking space in the area.
Sell it to a builder for houses.	Sell it to a property developer for a factory.	Build an industrial estate with factory or office units for letting to small businesses.

- Write a list of questions you need to ask in order to help you to decide the best action to take.

Teachers' note Ask the children why parks become derelict. Draw out that local councils have a limited budget and that sometimes there are other priorities for it. Ask them to consider all the possible actions that could be taken and to decide which they would take if they were the local council. They could hold a mock council meeting.

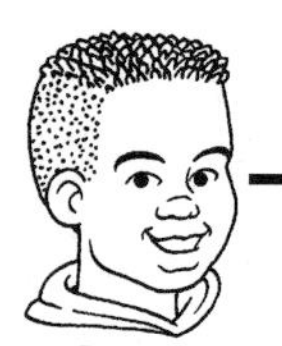

Coat of arms

When the Metropolitan Borough of Gateshead was formed in 1974, its coat of arms was designed by a primary school pupil.

Plough to symbolise the rural parts of the borough.

Cog to represent the tradition of industry in the area.

Helmet from the logo of Gateshead Council.

Crown (from the coat of arms of Durham County Council).

Portcullis (a strong gate). Many coats of arms have a portcullis.

Piece of railway line because Gateshead was an important railway centre.

Motto ('In unity, progress') because several areas were united to form Gateshead.

Most coats of arms have two 'supporters' – people or animals – holding up the shield.

- **Find out what these animals are and the term used for their stance.**

____

____

- **Draw the coat of arms of your nearest town.**
- **Label it like the one above.**

What does the coat of arms tell you about your locality?

- **Write an explanation.**

Teachers' note Use this page to introduce the significance of coats of arms. The children can find out more from www.gateshead.gov.uk/civtrad2.htm. As a homework activity, ask the children to find out if their city, town or village has a coat of arms or logo. What symbols are on it and what do they represent?

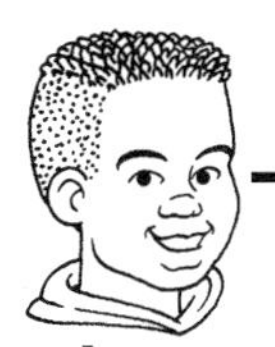

Local election

In a local election people can vote for their local councillor.

Before the election there is a campaign to gain support from the voters.

- **Choose the role of one of these candidates.**
- **Prepare what you will say in a role-play of a local election campaign.**

Yvette Sabu

Aged 35.
Married with two children aged 6 and 10.
Lecturer in music.

Priorities
Re-organising schools so that money is not wasted on empty classrooms and under-used equipment. Using the money saved to provide music tuition and instruments. Every child should have the opportunity to learn to play a musical instrument – not just the well-off.

Jason Smith

Aged 25.
Single.
Unemployed building worker.

Priorities
Providing care and accommodation for homeless people. There are at least 60 homeless people in this small town. They sleep in doorways and bus shelters and under bridges, even in the winter. Everyone deserves a roof over his or her head.

Myra Green

Aged 60.
Retired secretary.
Divorced with four grown-up children.

Priorities
Keeping our streets clean. Providing additional bins – especially where fast food wrappings are discarded – and free ‘pooper scoops’ at council offices, shops and in parks. Providing extra dog waste bins and moving any which are under-used or are too close to bus stops, shop doors or doors or windows of homes.

Omar Iqbal

Aged 50.
Engineer.
Married with a son aged 25 and a daughter aged 20.

Priorities
Improving the car parking facilities in the town centre by building an extra car park and reducing the time for which cars can be parked on the High Street by introducing a 2-hour limit for ‘pay and display’ areas.

- **Write a profile of yourself as a council candidate.**

Teachers' note Explain the difference between a general election (voting for a representative in Parliament) and a local election (voting for a representative on the local council). Point out that the local council looks after its own area and does not deal with law-making (see **Notes on the activities**, page 11). The children could work in groups of eight and enact the roles of the four candidates, a chairperson and three audience members, who could each ask the candidates a question.

Campaign leaflet

How would you persuade voters to elect you as a local councillor?

- **Plan a campaign leaflet.**

Photograph of yourself doing something useful.

Name ______________________

Age ______________________

Family details ______________________

____

____

Your connection with the place

The area where you live, school, membership of local clubs.

____

____

____

What makes you belong here

Ancestors, relations, how you or your family have supported the place.

____

____

____

What matters to you

____

____

____

- **Edit your leaflet.**
- **Decide which parts to highlight, and how.**
- **Print your leaflet using a computer.**

Teachers' note Ask the children to consider how they would encourage people to vote for them as a local council member. Point out that they need to demonstrate that they care about the local community through commitment to certain priorities and by establishing their connections with the area. For hints on campaign leaflets, see www.justdosomething.net/xsp/xsc.asp?uri=/home/find/elected/elected-as-a-local-councillor.

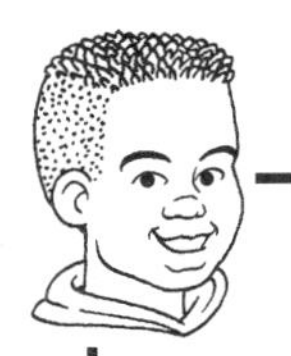

Eyesore

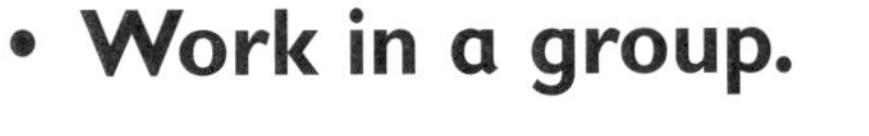

- **Work in a group.**

  What problems can be caused by a derelict building?

- **Discuss this with your group.**
- **List the main points of your discussion.**

Use bullet points.

Problems

- ______________________
- ______________________
- ______________________
- ______________________
- ______________________

What do you think should be done?

People to consult ______________________

____

____

Information to collect ______________________

____

____

Suggestions for action ______________________

____

____

Why is it important to consult people?

- **List the advantages of this.**

Teachers' note This can be used with any topical issue concerning local buildings: for example, vandalism or squatting. Ask the children if they have noticed any dilapidated buildings in the local area. Do they know what has happened to them and why no one takes care of them? Discuss whether the owners should be required to repair them or whether it is no one else's business. If it is the business of others, why? How does the building affect them? What can they do about it?

Council in action

A gang of young people have been hanging around the park and drinking beer.

Some local people phone Mrs Singh, their local councillor.

The park is littered with bottles and cans.
These youngsters are at risk. They are too young to buy alcohol. Also drug-dealers have begun to target them.
It is illegal to be drunk and disorderly like this.

- **Discuss with a partner what Mrs Singh could do.**

Problems	Solutions

Think about what else the young people can do.

Think about the law.

- **Write what you would do if you were the local councillor.**

- **Write a speech to present at a council meeting.**

How would your actions solve the problems...?

Teachers' note Tell the children that the residents of this place object to their neighbourhood being damaged in this way. Ask the children if their comments are justified. What can these people do? Ask them to consider what they would do if they were the local councillor. Point out that they should consider the causes of the problems and the people who cause them.

News sources

- **Compare the news in different national newspapers on one day.**

  Which events or issues are included?

  Why do you think different papers highlighted different stories?

- **Discuss your findings with a partner.**

You need

a collection of newspapers from the same day

	Newspaper ✔							
Issue or event	Daily Express	Financial Times	Guardian	Independent	Daily Mail	Times		

How do newspapers choose their headline stories?

- **Write an explanation.**

Teachers' note The children need a collection of the day's newspapers (see the suggested titles, which could be substituted if others are used instead). After they have completed the activity, invite feedback and ask them why they think some newspapers choose different stories for their main front page news. Point out that the headlines are what sell the newspaper and discuss the intended audiences of the newspapers.

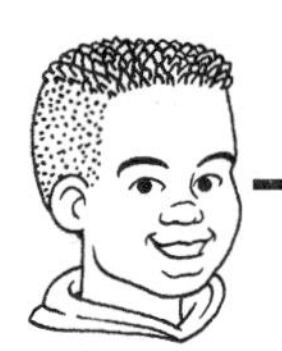

Breaking news

Anna McTavish, a reporter for a local television news programme, had this rushed phone call from a friend.

There's been a robbery – armed, I think – at Hareshill Post Office.
No one seems to have witnessed it. Postmistress was alone.
Had to hand over thousands – could be £36,000.
Seems a lot for a tiny place in the middle of nowhere.

Anna decided to find out more.

What facts should she check?

Date ______________________ **Place** ______________________

Facts to check

____

____

____

____

____

____

____

____

- **Find out about a local news event.**
  What facts would people want to know?
  What facts should be in the report?
- **Write a news report for the local television news.**

Teachers' note Invite a volunteer to read the quotation. Ask the children what facts are given and what suggestions are made. What does the speaker seem to think about the robbery? Discuss how the news should be reported. Draw out that those who report the news have a responsibility towards the readers and the people about whom they write. Point out that they also want a good story for their newspaper.

It's the way you tell it

- **Discuss the two newspaper reports with a partner.**
- **List the facts.**
- **Comment on the opinion each report presents.**

1 BLOT ON THE LANDSCAPE

Picturesque Ash Hill is just the latest beauty spot to be ruined in the urban sprawl of Dormtown. Twenty-six 'executive homes' will blight a piece of ancient parkland which has been enjoyed for more than a century by local people for weekend walks and picnics.

Not a single piece of local stone will be used. These houses would be the same if they were built a hundred miles away (pity they are not); the 'rustic' bricks and other materials come from Jerrybuild's central suppliers.

Wooden decking covers even the local soil in the manicured gardens.

2 EXCITING NEW DEVELOPMENT

Dormtown moves into the 21st century!

National builders Jerrybuild's prestigious new development at Ash Hill features all the 'must haves' of modern, yet rural, homes: ensuite and dressing room in the master bedroom, utility room, double garage and built-in barbecue. The image of dowdy Dormtown could soon be transformed from the baggy jumper, wellies and waxed jacket in a truck to the designer suit in a sleek Ferrari. This is a move upmarket.

Existing houses in the town could double in price as a result of this enterprising venture.

Watch this space!

	Opinions	
Facts	Report 1	Report 2

- **Re-write the report in a way that shows no bias or opinion.**

Teachers' note Mask the name of the place in the reports (Ash Hill). You could scan the passages using the optical character recognition function of the scanner and display them on an electronic whiteboard. Use EDIT and CUT to delete the place name and keep the document open. Invite volunteers to read the passages aloud. What impressions do they have of each place? Unmask the place name (or use EDIT and UNDO). Are the children surprised that they describe the same place?

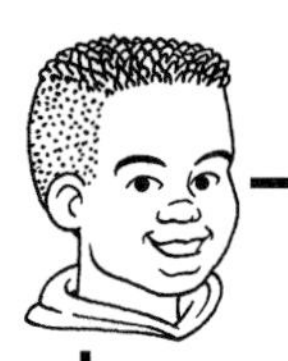

Documentary

- **Work in a group.**
- **Plan a documentary video about cycle paths in your local area.**

Do some research first.
What do you find?
How many are there?
Not enough?

Preliminary notes

____

____

____

On screen	Narrative (notes)
Introduction	
Cycle paths in use	
Roads that need cycle paths	
People's opinions	
Conclusion	

Make an impact.

Get the facts right.

Interview people.

Make your message clear.

Now try this!

- **Use data-handling software to record and present evidence about the need for more cycle paths in your area.**

Teachers' note This activity could be used in connection with any topical issue instead of cycle paths, but cycle paths are an issue that affects children directly. Take the children to carry out a survey of local cycle paths and to find out whether people think there should be more. They could also investigate local roads where there is no provision for cyclists and compare their findings.

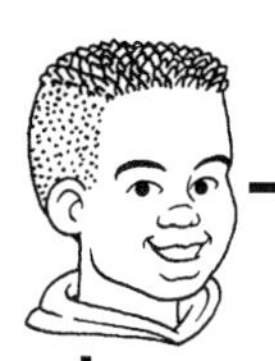

Turning points

- **On the signposts, write about some big changes in your life.**

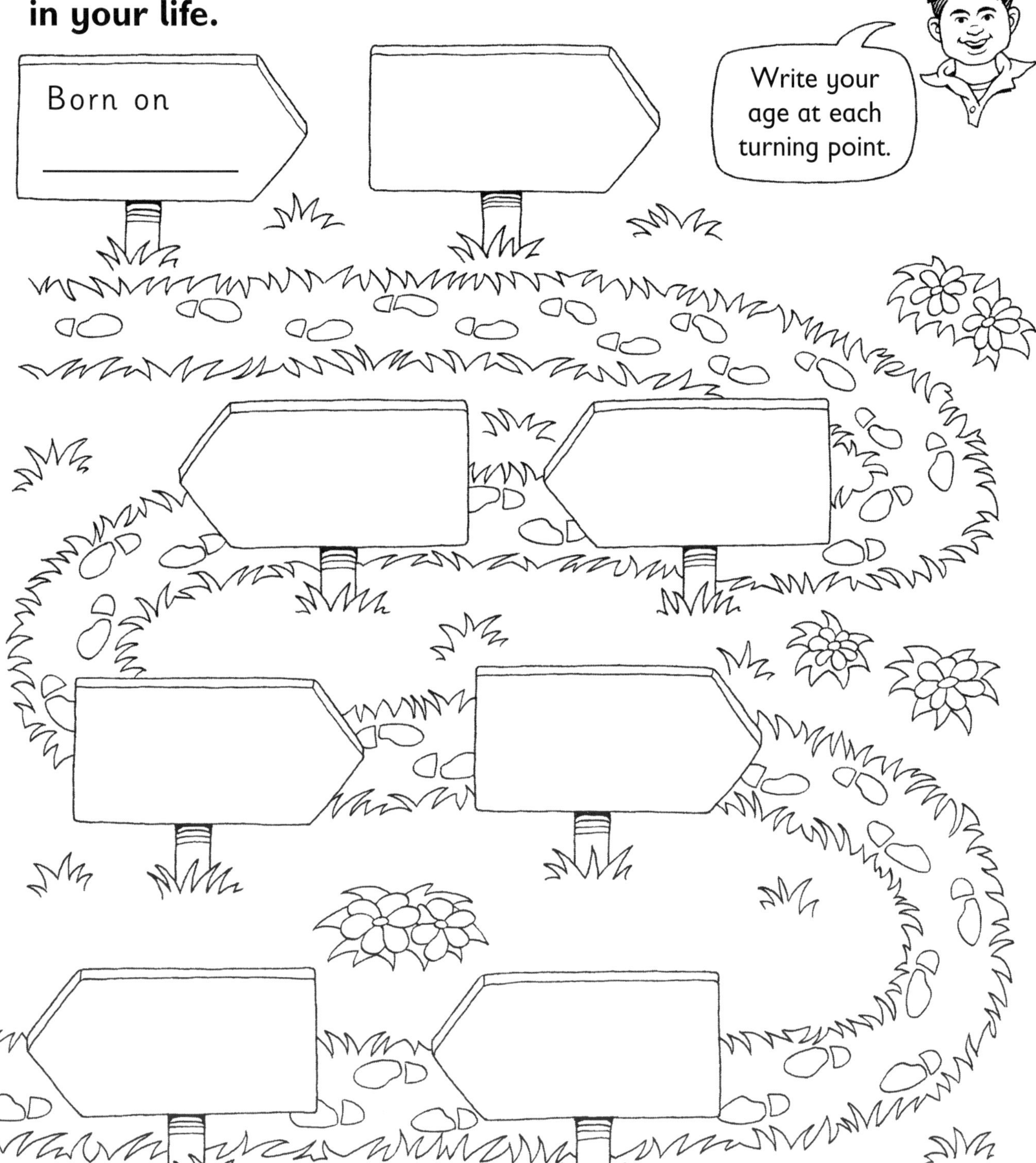
Born on
Write your age at each turning point.

Now try this!

- **Draw a signpost for the next important change you will make.**
- **Discuss your feelings about it with a partner.**

Teachers' note Ask the children to think about significant times in their lives, when something important happened which marked a change from one stage in their lives to another: for example, starting nursery school, having an operation, being old enough to join a club or group. Which of these 'turning points' do they remember looking forward to? Do they remember how they felt when they reached them?

New school

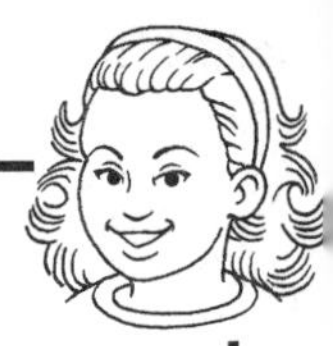

- **Work with a partner.**
- **Think about moving to secondary school.**
- **Discuss:**
  - **what you are looking forward to.**
  - **what you are worrying about.**

We are looking forward to

We are worrying about

- **List some ways in which you and others in the class can help one another to prepare for your new school.**

Teachers' note Ask the children about the next turning point they are likely to face. Focus on moving to secondary school. The children could interview their partners about their feelings about this and make notes about what they say. Afterwards draw out the main things to look forward to and make a list of the main points which worry the children. Discuss how to deal with these (see **Notes on the activities**, page 12).

Question time

What do you know about your new school?

What do you want to know?

- **Discuss this with a partner.**

Think about … … location … … friends … … teachers … … rooms … … travel … … homework … … uniform … … rules … … subjects …

What I know	My questions

- **Find the answers from the school's prospectus, website and pupils you know.**

- **Organise an information-sharing system for children going on to the same school.**

Teachers' note Point out that many of the concerns children raise before moving to secondary school result from not knowing what to expect. Emphasise that we all feel more confident about situations when we are well informed. The children's questions could be e-mailed to their new schools or discussed during a visit there, or teachers and pupils from the schools could be invited to talk to the children.

Firm friends

Now you are ready to move on to your next school!

- **Use this page to help you remember your friends.**

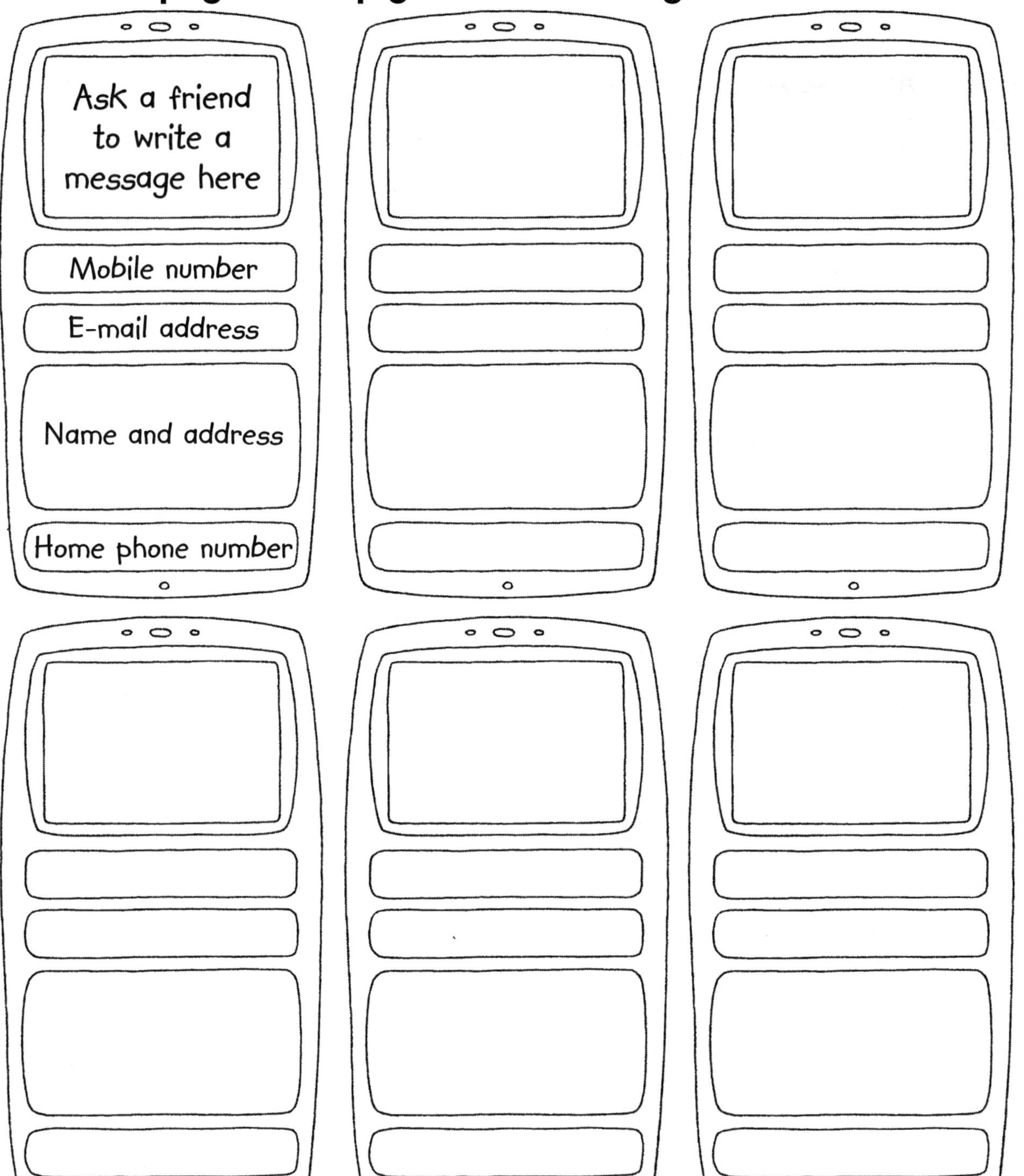

What can new Year 7 pupils do to support one another?

- **Write your ideas.**

Teachers' note This activity is designed to form a memento of the children's last day in Year 6. Allow them time to write messages for one another and provide additional copies of the page as necessary.